19/50.

Anglian Blood

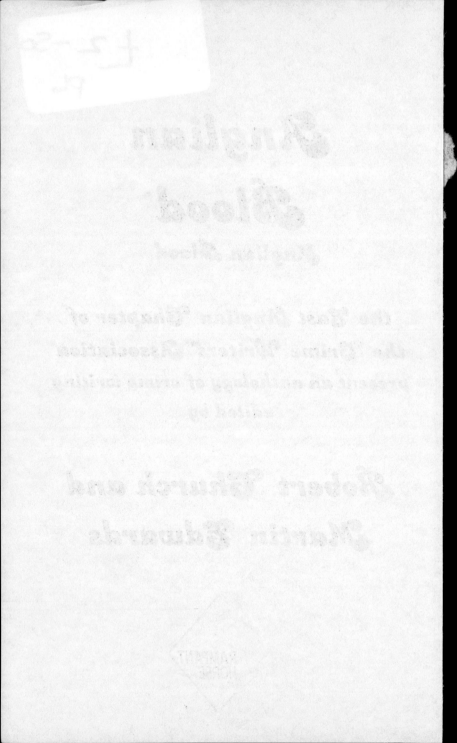

Anglian Blood

the East Anglian Chapter of
the Crime Writers' Association
present an anthology of crime writing
edited by

Robert Church and
Martin Edwards

RAMPANT
HORSE

First published in Great Britain in 1995
by Rampant Horse Limited
140 Whitehall Road Norwich Norfolk NR2 3EW

Copyright © compilation, R Church and M Edwards
copyright © individual contributions, contributors

Set in 11 pt Times Roman
Cover design: Chris Redman/Images
Cover illustration: Stephen Read
A CIP catalogue record for this book is available from the British Library

ISBN 1-898839-09-3

Acknowledgements

The article by P D James, *Is There Arsenic Still for Tea?* is a revised
version of a piece which first appeared in *The Countryman* magazine.
A version of the article by Robert Church, *Seventeenth Century Justice:
The Trial of the Lowestoft Witches,* first appeared in *The Criminologist.*

Printed and bound in Great Britain by Bookcraft (Bath) Ltd.

Contents

Foreword 7

Introduction 11

Is there Arsenic Still for Tea? *P D James* 21

Dead End *John Harman* 27

The Inside Man *Clare Dawson* 49

Dodgy, Very *James Melville* 63

Flat Share *Judith Saxton* 79

Just a Bit of Fun *Rosemary Walker* 95

Seventeenth-Century Justice: The Trial of the
Lowestoft Witches *Robert Church* 111

A Hank of Hair *Jean McConnell* 125

Killing Little William *Carole Rawcliffe* 151

Listeners *Margaret Moore* 165

An Odd Coincidence *James Pattinson* 185

The Bedell Virgin *Ann Quinton* 195

A Job for Life *Martin Edwards* 207

Why they Didn't Hang Pitcher *Alan Hunter* 217

In at the Deep End *Vivien Armstrong* 231

Two's Company *Sonia Kinahan* 247

In memory of Nancy Livingston

Foreword

The fact that the Crime Writers' Association has an East Anglian Chapter which is vigorous enough and enterprising enough to launch an anthology of crime writing, fictional and non-fictional, of its own, is an indication of how healthy the current state really is, not just of the CWA but of British crime writing and reading in general.

The CWA was formed by John Creasey forty-one years ago as a social group in London, where crime writers could meet once a month after work to discuss their art and to further the image of crime writing generally. It has since grown into a nationwide and international association four hundred strong. Its regional chapters meet regularly and form staunch local relationships which have resulted in many original activities as well as anthologies of this kind.

Ask your local public librarian which is the fiction section most universally popular among men and women equally and he or she will promptly reply, 'crime'. The state of crime fiction has never been more popular or more universally appreciated. It is true that television has given great impetus to the form, but the excellent television series and individual programmes which are so widely viewed represent, in many ways, only the tip of an iceberg of enormous variety available to the public.

The current practitioners of crime writing in Britain can in no way be described as all traditional, parish-pump genre writers of predictable books, whether fictional or non-fictional. The scope and the scale of crime writing has never been greater than it is today, and many readers and critics feel that we may indeed be passing through an expansion of the so-called 'Golden Age' which will be seen as remarkable in years to come.

It must not be thought, however, that a narrow nationalist view of crime writing prevails in the Association. The Annual Awards of the CWA, which culminate in the CWA Gold Dagger Award for the best crime novel of the year, have seen authors from the USA, Scandinavia and many other countries featuring in the short lists for the awards, which are open to all crime writers. In 1993 the winner was Patricia Cornwell of the USA and in 1994 the short list featured three British, three American and one Danish writer. The winners were Minette Walters for *The Scold's Bridle* (fiction) and David Canter for *Criminal Shadows* (non-fiction). We believe that these awards represent the very best being published today.

The crime story, whether fictional or an account of true crime, can be used to express a variety of views, social, economic, ethical, humorous, political and philosophical, quite apart from its other slants on human behaviour. It must, however, always be entertaining and engaging, otherwise the reader rapidly loses interest.

In this compilation of the work of East Anglian members and other welcome crime writers there is no shortage of entertainment, variety and interest. The fact that all the stories are set in East Anglia does not limit their scope nor their remarkably high standards, and strikes a strong personal chord, since my own last novel was set largely in the area. I am sure, therefore, that every reader will find this anthology engaging, entertaining and in the varied, versatile style of which we of the CWA are extremely proud.

John Malcolm
Chairman, Crime Writers' Association

Introduction

Generations of crime writers have found in East Anglia a fertile source of inspiration for their mysteries. The aim of this anthology is to show that crime writing in the region continues to thrive as well as, perhaps, to cast a little light on the reasons why such a tranquil part of the United Kingdom should have provided a setting for so many stories of death and detection.

It does seem strange, at first sight, that East Anglia should have been the scene of celebrated mysteries by authors ranging from Wilkie Collins and Sir Arthur Conan Doyle in the Victorian era to Ruth Rendell and P D James in the present day. The region takes in not only Norfolk and Suffolk but also parts of Cambridgeshire and Essex and encompasses seaside resorts, peaceful market towns and rich agricultural pastures. Yet much of the landscape has a mysterious quality which continues to appeal to imaginative writers. The rural idyll was, moreover, put into perspective by Sherlock Holmes in *The Copper Beeches* when he famously said, 'It is my belief, Watson, founded upon my experience, that the lowest and vilest alleys in London do not present a more dreadful record of sin than does the smiling and beautiful countryside.'

Holmes' very first investigation, during his student days,

took place in Norfolk. In *The 'Gloria Scott'*, he recounts to Watson the story of his visit to a friend's family who lived in a little hamlet 'in the country of the Broads': a case with a tragic end. Holmes returned to Norfolk to investigate the mystery of *The Dancing Men,* after being consulted by Mr Hilton Cubitt ('my people have been at Ridling Thorpe for a matter of five centuries, and there is no better-known family in the county'), about the cryptic messages in code that were terrifying his wife. A common theme in both stories is that past wrongdoings return to haunt those who thought they had escaped forever and found peace and safety in a new life in East Anglia.

During the Golden Age of detective fiction between the Wars, the action in a number of memorable novels took place there. *Death Under Sail,* published in 1932, was the first novel of C P Snow. It is a classic 'closed circle' murder mystery: six guests are detailed on their murdered host's wherry half-way through a holiday on the Broads. One of them, it is clear, is guilty of killing Roger Mills and, as the enigmatic amateur detective Finbow points out, all of them hated the dead man. Snow evokes the landscape with care and skill and it is a pity that he deserted the genre for almost half a century, preferring to concentrate on his scientific work and the *Strangers and Brothers* sequence of novels.

John Leslie Palmer and Hilary Aidan St George Saunders wrote thrillers and detective novels together under the pseudonym of Francis Beeding and two of their finest mysteries benefit from being firmly located in East Anglia. *The Norwich Victims* boasts an ingenious twist, a subtle clue to which may possibly be discerned from the gimmick of having photographs of the chief characters reproduced at the beginning of the book. Even better is *Death Walks in Eastrepps*, in which a baffling series of murders takes place in an East Coast holiday resort at the height of the season.

The atmosphere of the town is splendidly captured, but at no cost in terms of pace or readability. The murderer's motive is intriguing and it is a pity that the book is so little known today.

A classic mystery novel set (so internal evidence suggests) on the Isle of Ely is *The Nine Tailors* by Dorothy L Sayers, which begins with Lord Peter Wimsey finding himself stranded on New Year's Eve following a car accident. He takes refuge in the village of Fenchurch St Paul, where he becomes engrossed in the lives of the local bell-ringers and eventually learns the identity of the killer of the faceless and handless corpse found in the local churchyard. Margery Allingham – like Sayers a major detective novelist who was also a long-time resident of the region – set several books in Suffolk, including *The Crime at Black Dudley* and *Look to the Lady,* which have been regularly reprinted in recent years.

The doyen of East Anglian writers in the post-war period is Alan Hunter. Norfolk born, he began his long series of books about that sympathetic policeman George Gently as long ago as 1955, with *Gently Does It.* In an introductory comment to an essay about his work in *Twentieth Century Crime and Mystery Writers,* he said, 'I found the environment of a dramatic situation a critical factor in its evocation: this time, this place, belonged to these characters, this mystery. And so I choose a location which is directly familiar to me, usually one I have known for many years. As a result my books are set mostly in East Anglia...' *Gently Floating,* with a setting on the Broads, is one of several of his novels which are strengthened by a vivid depiction of the regional background.

The work of Jonathan Gash and Sheila Radley has also benefited from the authors' knowledge of East Anglia and their sensitive use of it as a setting for their stories. Gash burst on to the scene in 1977 with *The Judas Pair*, which won the Crime Writers Association's John Creasey Memorial Award for the best first crime novel of that year. The book introduced that rascally antiques dealer Lovejoy, and the success of Gash's series has been crowned by the popularity of the adaptations of his books for television starring Ian McShane.

Radley has been less prolific but her novels about Detective Chief Inspector Douglas Quantrill have nevertheless won an appreciative readership. Quantrill made his debut in *Death and the Maiden,* and the opening paragraphs of that book memorably contrast the peacefulness of rural Suffolk with the discovery of an eighteen-year-old girl's body in a shallow river. As a fellow crime writer, Essex-born Robert Barnard, has aptly put it in a critical appreciation, 'Radley gives a picture of village life that is neither sentimentalised nor condescended to.'

S T Haymon is a local writer whose infrequent novels featuring Inspector Ben Jurnet have been much praised. Angleby, the main town of the district in which he is based, bears a close resemblance to Norwich, and *Ritual Murder* earned the CWA Silver Dagger Award.

Remarkably, East Anglia has been the setting for two modern crime novels which rank amongst the most dazzling ever written. Ruth Rendell, who lives in Suffolk and has written a book about the county, has located several of her mysteries in her home territory, but especially brilliant is *A Fatal Inversion,* written under the name of Barbara Vine. The compelling first chapter ends with the discovery of the skeletons of a woman and a small child in the animal cemetery at Wyvis Hall. It becomes clear that a crime was committed at the Hall during the long hot summer of 1976, and Rendell/Vine's description of the relationships between the young people who camped out there at that time is exceptionally suspenseful.

P D James, in her most welcome contribution to this anthology, explains how East Anglia has fired her imagination and inspired some of her best-known work. Outstanding even by her high standards is *Devices and Desires,* which is set on the remote Larksoken headland on the North Sea coast, a place of dramatic contrast between the broken arches of the ruined Benedictine Abbey and the great grey bulk of a nuclear power station which looms over the quiet place 'like a grandiose modern monument to the unknown dead'. Rarely has any scene of crime been portrayed with such power.

Apart from being the setting for many crime stories, East Anglia has had its share of real-life murders. In 1826 the shooting of Maria Marten, a mole catcher's daughter, by her lover William Corder at Polstead in Essex, was the true stuff of melodrama. The event captured the public's imagination at the time, and has since become part of the region's folklore.

Two well-documented murders occurred at the turn of the century. The relationship between the ex-soldier Samuel Henry Dougal and the Catholic gentlewoman Camille Cecile Holland which began in 1898 was an ill-matched liaison which ended tragically a year later when Dougal shot Camille at their farm near Clavering. Benefiting from Miss Holland's modest fortune while living the life of a country gentleman after the murder, Dougal was unmasked four years later when a discarded lady friend voiced to the police her suspicions regarding Camille Holland's disappearance.

A thorough search of Moat Farm eventually unearthed Camille's remains from a farmyard grave. Meanwhile Dougal, who had departed for a weekend in Bournemouth with his current lady friend, was arrested soon afterwards in London. Found guilty at Essex Assizes in June 1903, Dougal was reported to have confessed his guilt on the gallows the following month.

The other crime took place on a wild and stormy night at the end of May 1902, when Rose Harsent, a servant girl, had her throat cut at the home of her employer at Peasenhall in Suffolk. Suspicion immediately centred on William Gardiner, a well-respected member of the village community who, according to rumour, had been carrying on an illicit affair with the murdered girl.

Gardiner was arrested for the murder and was tried for the first time in November 1902 at Ipswich. At the end of four days the jury were unable to agree, so a retrial was ordered. Another stalemate was reached at the end of the second trial in January 1903.

Gardiner was spared a third ordeal after the Director of Public Prosecutions ruled against another trial. Soon afterwards Gardiner, together with his wife and their six children, left Peasenhall to start a new life elsewhere, leaving for ever unanswered the question as to whether or not he had killed Rose Harsent.

Nowadays the killing of a policeman fails to provoke the horror and condemnation that accompanied the cold-blooded murder of a village constable in September 1927. Two former gaol-birds, Frederick Guy Browne and William Kennedy, had left London on a nocturnal expedition into Essex, where they had broken into a doctor's garage in Billericay and stolen his motor car. Driving along a remote country road near Stapleford Abbots on their way back to London, they were stopped by PC George Gutteridge. Sensing the policeman's increasing suspicion at their replies to his questions, one of the men drew a .45 Webley service revolver and twice shot him. As Gutteridge lay stricken by the roadside, the gunman bent over him and fired two more shots, one through each eye.

A nationwide hunt for the killers, led by Detective Chief Superintendent William Berrett, eventually bore fruit four months later when Browne was arrested at his Battersea garage. Incriminating items including the murder weapon, cartridges, a mask and a false driving licence were recovered at the same time. Five days later, following a tip-off, William Kennedy was arrested in Liverpool where he had fled with his wife.

The two men were tried at the Old Bailey in April 1928 before Mr Justice Avory. Although each protested his innocence, they were both found guilty and executed on the last day of May.

Two murders involving servicemen are still recalled by some older inhabitants of East Anglia. In November 1944 the body of a twenty-seven year old member of the Women's Auxiliary Air Force was found lying in a ditch at Ellough near Beccles in Suffolk. She had been raped and suffocated. The previous evening Winifred Evans, a wireless operator, had been to a dance at an American air force base before returning to her quarters to change into uniform prior to setting out on a lonely mile-long walk to her post where she was due on the night shift.

At about the same time a thirty-seven year old airman, Arthur Heys, had been discovered loitering half drunk in the women's ablutions. He was summarily redirected by a WAAF corporal to his own quarters, and departed on the road taken by Winifred Evans a few minutes earlier.

Chief Inspector 'Ted' Greeno, the Scotland Yard detective heading the enquiry, faced with the formidable task of tracing the suspect from among the thousands of servicemen based in the area, hit upon the idea of having the WAAF corporal who had spoken to the intruder on the night of the murder attend the suspect's pay parade. The corporal had no hesitation in identifying Heys as he stepped forward to collect his money.

Although the circumstantial and forensic evidence for the

prosecution was impressive, Heys clinched the case against himself by smuggling a letter out of Norwich prison while he was on remand. It was addressed to his commanding officer and was purportedly from the true killer of Winifred Evans. The letter, however, contained details which could have been known only to the perpetrator of the crime, so despite the best efforts of his counsel to discredit the other evidence, the letter he himself had written effectively sent Heys to the gallows.

Fourteen years later a USAAF master sergeant stationed at Sculthorpe in Norfolk was more fortunate. Marcus M Marymont, a married man living on the base with his wife Helen and their three children, fell in love with a married Englishwoman, Cynthia Taylor, during one of his frequent official forays to the USAAF headquarters at Bushey Park on the outskirts of London. Initially the affair flourished, but after several months increasing financial pressure on Marymont, and rumours circulating among his colleagues and neighbours, placed a strain on the relationship. Matters came to a head on the day Helen Marymont discovered an unposted love letter written by her husband to Cynthia Taylor.

Confronted by his wife with this damning evidence, Marymont decided to precipitate a course of action that it seems he had already embarked upon. Helen Marymont became increasingly ill with vomiting and diarrhoea, and eventually died in agony on 26 May 1958. A subsequent post-mortem revealed that she had been poisoned. Knowledge of Marymont's infidelity, and of his deteriorating family situation, left little doubt in the minds of the authorities as to who had administered the arsenic.

Court martialled in December 1958, Marcus Marymont was found guilty. As there was not the required unanimity among the adjudicating officers to impose the death penalty, he was sentenced to hard labour for life. In 1960 this was reduced to thirty-five years by the United States Court of Military Appeals.

Since the 1950s several other sensational murder cases have made headlines throughout the region. The shooting of Mrs Muriel Patience together with the attempted murder of her husband and daughter in 1972, in what became known as The Barn Murder at Braintree; the 1976 killing of anti-blood sports campaigner and naturalist William Sweet in a Cambridgeshire beauty spot, and the slaughter of Nevil and June Bamber, their step-daughter Sheila and her two young sons at White House Farm in south Essex in 1985 are among the more well-known.

These real-life regional crimes, together with their fictional counterparts, give the lie to the popular conception of East Anglia as a peaceful part of the country. They not only illustrate the appeal of the region as a setting for crime novels, but reveal the fact that violent death can often lurk in even the most attractive corners of our land.

Finally, we wish to thank those who have written stories for this anthology; John Malcolm, the current Chairman of the Crime Writers' Association for contributing a foreword, and Susan Curran and her colleagues at Rampant Horse Ltd for their co-operation and efficiency in producing a book which, we hope, will entertain and stimulate interest in both fictional and real-life crime in East Anglia.

Robert Church
Martin Edwards

Is there Arsenic Still for Tea?

P D James

P D James was born in Oxford, and was formerly a civil servant. Her books include *Cover Her Face, Shroud for a Nightingale, Unnatural Causes, An Unsuitable Job for a Woman, The Black Tower, Death of an Expert Witness, Innocent Blood, The Skill Beneath the Skin, A Taste for Death, Devices and Desires,* and most recently *Original Sin.* She was awarded the OBE in 1983 and was made a DBE in 1991. She is a Fellow of the Royal Society of Arts and of the Royal Society of Literature, and an Associate Fellow of Downing College, Cambridge.

Nearly all my novels have had their beginnings in a part of England and in a moment of intense response to its spirit and atmosphere. And because I am a crime-writer, dealer in fictional death and fabricator of mystery, my country, however familiar, beautiful and well-loved, inevitably becomes dangerous territory.

Such for me is East Anglia, setting for four of my books, and, in particular, that stretch of sea-denuded coast between Lowestoft and Aldeburgh. I am not at home with mountains. I gaze in awe at their majesty and grandeur but I find them intimidating and claustrophobic. What I love are the wide skies of the eastern seaboard, the strong yet subtle colours of the landscape, the sense of space and isolation, the bird life of the wide estuaries and the marshes, reed beds quivering against still water and always, familiar yet menacing, the resonance of the North Sea.

No part of England can have been more influenced by the sea than this part of Suffolk. In the Middle Ages it gave to the area prosperity, trade, food, learning and piety. And then, year after year, its devastating waves reclaimed from the land what it had given: choked its harbours, drowned its fine churches and monasteries, destroyed its coastline and overlaid prosperity with barren sand.

It is difficult for the holiday-maker to realise that the small and charming resorts of Southwold, Orford and Aldeburgh were once thriving ports and that Dunwich, now a few cottages above a shingled beach, was once a flourishing maritime city which, according to Stowe, 'LXX pryshe churches, howses of religion, hoppitalls and chapelles, and as many wynde mells and toppe scheppes', a city which, until 1832, sent two members to Parliament. Small wonder that, standing at dusk on Dunwich beach, I can imagine the tolling of bells from drowned steeples and hear the echo of plain-song on the still air.

It was one evening on Dunwich beach that my crime-writer's imagination gave me the idea for my third book. I pictured a small dinghy drifting oarless on the tide and bearing one hapless voyager, a neatly dressed corpse with his hands severed at the wrists. And it was this frightening and some would say, morbid image which was the beginning of *Unnatural Causes*.

Today this is a coast of contrast. I can stand on the shore at Sizewell Gap, gaze out to sea past the small fishing boats drawn up on the shingle and know that I am seeing the same sight as met the eyes of eighteenth-century smugglers huddled among the dunes and watching for the first sail. And then I turn my eyes to the north and see, within a stone's throw, the huge, squat modernity of Sizewell atomic power station, a silent and potent symbol of a power even more terrifying than the sea. Similarly, I can sit chatting to the old sailors in their reading-room on Southwold cliff, surrounded by ships' figureheads and the fading photographs of great storms and oilskinned heroes, then have my ears blasted by the roar of low-flying military aircraft from the East Anglian bases. But, curiously enough, these intrusions of our age emphasise rather than destroy the sense this coast gives me of peace and remoteness, of a landscape which, though always at the mercy of the sea and always changing, seems eternally the same.

One does not always look for a sinister setting when writing a detective story. Often a beautiful and peaceful place can provide that contrast which enhances terror. W H Auden, who loved the genre, could not read a detective story with pleasure unless it was set in an English village or small town. The setting, he wrote, should be the Great Good Place, an innocent society in a state of grace; the more Eden-like it was, the greater the contrast and horror of murder. In the fast-action thriller the story is often set in a foreign or exotic location and the hero's exploits take place against a background of torrid tropical beaches, Continental casinos or sinister châteaux. But the writer of detective stories more often prefers malice domestic, the ordinary and comforting rendered frightening and alien, the familiar overlaid with menace. To parody Rupert Brooke:

Stands the church clock at ten to three?

And is there arsenic still for tea?

For me, in any crime novel, the setting is of immense importance. It establishes mood, enhances atmosphere, helps anchor the plot in reality and influences both the story and the characterisation. Because of its importance and the need to make it as real to the reader as it is to me, I could never set a novel in an unfamiliar place. And however familiar, I like to revisit it when the book is in progress, to breathe the spirit of the place as I do its air, to make notes on the flora and fauna, on the landscape and architecture, on the colour and texture of the soil and to watch the effect of changing light on countryside and buildings. How fortunate I am to have been born in a county which offers its artists and its writers such diversity, such richness and such beauty.

Dead End

John Harman

John Harman was born in Harrow in 1942 and was a journalist for ten years, working on regional newspapers in the UK and America and finally on *The Times*. He has also worked as a journalist in television, and in the advertising, publishing and conference industries. His first thriller, *Money For Nothing,* was published in 1988, and it was followed by *The Bottom Line* and *Called to Account.* His wife Abigail is a professional photographer. They have five grown-up children and live in a large late-Georgian house in Little Shelford near Cambridge.

No one knew where she was buried.

Except, of course, the man who'd killed her.

Everybody, or at least everybody who remembered the case, was sure Maxine Cashman was dead. She'd been dead for more than fourteen years. A man was serving life for her murder. *Had been* serving life for her murder.

I got the call early.

'You heard the news?' His was a generation that listened to the news.

'I saw it on the seven-thirty bulletin.'

'Can you come up? Today?'

I pulled a face and stared at the walls of my office. 'What's the point, Ronald? They'll catch him before the day's out. He's been inside for fourteen years. He's institutionalised. Where's he going to go?'

'But you know him. Maybe you can get to him before the police. Maybe, outside, he'll talk to you.'

I told him it wasn't likely but he was as persuasive as ever and in the end I went.

His part of Essex wasn't like Essex at all. At least not the Essex I knew. As a kid in the fifties I'd known the arterial road to Southend and the salty taste of whelks on the crowded, kiss-me-quick beaches. Later, I'd got to know that part of the county north of Dunmow where famous pop stars and successful gangsters had started to make a habit of retiring. I'd even got to know the Essex new towns... the ruins of busted yuppiedom and the focus of dirty jokes about Sharon and Tracy.

Ronald Cashman's part of Essex was something out of a tourist brochure, with picturesque cottages snuggling around winsome village greens. He lived near Dedham, in a timber-framed cottage with a thatched roof. It was close to the river and next to the village cricket pitch. Very pretty – if you liked that kind of thing.

He was agitated when I got there but offered coffee and left me alone in the lounge whilst he went to make it. On a wall was a large-scale map of East Anglia. The numerous red crosses on it marked the places where Ronald Cashman had been digging for his daughter's body. His wife had helped him for the first few years and then given up, preferring to contract cancer and die painfully rather than actually find what remained of Maxine's body. Ronald had mourned her for a week and then gone back to his obsessive searching.

The media made something of him for a while but had got bored and left him to his grisly digging. He had been arrested twice and prosecuted for trespass half a dozen times but nothing would stop him. Every few months I'd get a call telling me that he had finally worked out where Robert Powlyn had buried his daughter. At first I'd tried dissuading him, but after a few years I'd stopped wasting my time. Cashman was as intractable as the shovel he constantly carried in the boot of his car.

I stared at the map.

On the night it happened Powlyn had been pulled over by Customs coming off the ferry at Harwich. He was a suspected trafficker of Class A and Customs had an idea he was carrying a couple of kilos of coke from Rotterdam. They'd searched his car, found nothing and let him go. Early the next morning he'd been found on the outskirts of Ipswich, bombed out of his mind and covered in blood – Maxine Cashman's blood. Her handbag and suitcase were in his car and so was a spade, smeared with blood and hair.

It was fifteen miles from the Harwich ferry to where they'd found Powlyn. Yet the car's milometer showed he'd done almost three hundred miles since Customs, who'd taken a note of his mileage, had pulled him in.

Even without a body he was charged with murder. The prosecution maintained that Powlyn had spotted Maxine on the ferry. She had a job with NATO in Brussels and was coming home on leave. Powlyn had chatted her up and somehow persuaded her into his car where he had killed her. Afterwards he had driven somewhere – God knows where – and buried her. The car mileage meant he could have buried her almost anywhere in East Anglia. The case against him was damning. A man I'd known had testified he'd seen Powlyn stop to help Maxine fix her car.

Powlyn's defence was pathetic. He'd already been half-stoned when he'd come off the ferry and everything afterwards, he said, was a blur. From what he could remember, he'd been attacked by some men who had forcibly injected him with more dope. After that he recalled nothing, except that he thought he'd heard someone say he was in Oostende. All he knew for certain was that he hadn't murdered Maxine.

The jury thought the story nonsense. There was no record of Powlyn sailing for Oostende that night and his testimony about the men assaulting him was obviously a fairy tale. They found him guilty and he got life.

Cashman returned with the coffee.

'If you find him before the police he might tell you,' he said. 'After all, he knows you.'

He sat down. I hadn't seen him in over a year and I noticed his hand shaking as he poured the coffee. That was new. He was looking old, the lines on his face more deeply scoured and his few remaining wisps of hair wafting snow white over his scalp. He had been a big man when I'd first known him; tragedy had turned him into a gnome.

I shrugged. 'I've seen him seven times in twelve years, Ronald. Not once did he tell me anything he hadn't said at his trial.'

'But he may return to the scene. He may go back to where he buried her.'

I told him I doubted it. 'What puzzles me,' I went on, 'is why he made the break. He must be coming up for parole soon.' An anguished look passed over Cashman's face. 'Why screw it up?'

'It doesn't matter. What matters is to find him. Find him and make him talk.' He paused. 'He may have gone back home.'

'That's the first place the police will look. Anyway, home is a prison out in the fens.'

'Well, wherever he's gone, you must find him.' Cashman was insistent.

I didn't want the job. Hadn't wanted it for years. In the

31

early days on my own I'd needed it. And I'd wanted to help the Cashmans. But now... now it all seemed so pitiful.

'I'll pay,' he added.

I said I didn't want his money but promised I'd spend a couple of days trying to find Powlyn before the police. Not that I held out much hope. I asked to use his phone. I needed to talk to some people who knew some people.

The calls took almost an hour. Afterwards Cashman tried to push a cheque on me. I told him to keep it. Taking his money was too ghoulish. I said I'd be in touch.

I headed north-west, over the river and into south Suffolk. It was late March and the day was overcast, the clumps of trees across the gently sloping fields stark and skeletal, their black limbs filigreed against a sky as grey as armour plate. I guessed that in summer it would be pretty countryside... a good place for people who liked the country. I drove through it quickly.

I got to the A45 at Bury St Edmunds and turned west, passing a monstrous sugar refinery, ugly enough to be something out of Soviet Russia. A real Joe Stalin special. The heavy lorries thundering towards the East coast ports were coming down the opposite carriageway like artillery shells.

I came off the road just before Cambridge. Bobby Powlyn had lived in a large village north of the city, out towards Ely. I reached it and drove slowly along a long main street of small, drab houses built of the local, dirty yellow, brick. The place was as alive and interesting as a puddle. A person would go to great lengths to get out of it. Maybe not as far as Powlyn, I thought, but...

Two beefy men were cramped inside a dark blue Mondeo, watching a terraced house across the street. Police. If they'd had sirens, flashing blue lights and a barrage balloon attached to the car they couldn't have advertised themselves more obviously. They watched as I drove past. It was clear Powlyn wasn't at the house – and that he wasn't going back either. The blokes in the car probably knew that.

I kept going, through Ely and beyond Queen Adelaide. Powlyn's prison was far out in the Fens. The roads were long and straight. One had a grass bank about fifteen feet high running for miles along its left side. The dark, brooding ridge looked like Offa's dyke. On its other side was one of the canals which sliced through the fen country like shiny knives. The locals called them levels.

Away to my right the dull, surly earth stretched flat and featureless all the way to the sky, not a tree or bush in sight. Cashman had done a lot of digging round here, searching for Maxine's remains. Nothing had come of it. You could bury the population of Britain in the Fens and never find a trace. The place gave me the creeps, miles of sky and sod all else.

The prison was out beyond March, in the middle of nowhere. It was incongruous and ugly, though not as ugly as the sugar refinery. Nearby was a village with a pub where the deputy warden had agreed to meet me. It was near closing time and the place was empty. Apart from a few faded prints of wildfowlers freezing their backsides off in duck punts, it was bare. A man followed me into the bar. He was short and powerfully built. It was the deputy warden.

We shook hands. 'What can I get you?' He asked for a double whisky. I had the same.

'We've agreed this is all off the record,' he said flatly when I brought the drinks over.

'Yes.'

He appraised me. 'You've been helping Maxine's father since the beginning, haven't you?'

'Almost. I was at the docks the night she came off the ferry. He heard later that I'd gone private and contacted me... asked me to help.'

'What were you doing at the docks?'

'Surveillance. Watching for suspected IRA coming in from the continent.'

He raised his eyebrows. 'What were you, Special Branch?'

I shook my head. 'Army. Intelligence. I did seven years hard but when I told them I wasn't signing up for another stint, they started giving me all the dirty jobs. Like catching pneumonia at Harwich docks.'

'Didn't you testify at the trial? That you'd seen Powlyn helping Maxine with her car?'

'No. That was a bloke called Geoffrey Templeton. Another intelligence man. He was a major in my unit before he moved across to a special unit, attached to Five. He was a *real* spook. He and his men had something big on that night.' I laughed. 'Harwich was packed with spooks. It was like Hallowe'en.'

'You know that Powlyn has always denied Templeton's testimony,' the warden said seriously.

I shrugged. 'Yeah, I know. But doesn't everyone on the inside claim they're innocent?' The warden sipped his drink and said nothing. 'Anyway,' I went on,' how the hell did he get away?'

It was the warden's turn to shrug. 'He was in the rehab unit. We were getting him ready for parole... life on the outside. It's more like an open prison there. It's easy enough to escape if you have help and a mind to. Nobody usually has a mind to.'

'So why did he go over the wall?'

'God knows. Powlyn was a model prisoner. He was undergoing a new form of therapy and he'd really started to get his head together. He'd always refused treatment before. Not only that, but a solicitor is pushing for a new trial for him. She claims there's been a miscarriage of justice. He's crazy to have made the break. Escaping jeopardises everything. He must have been talked into it by his friends.'

'Friends?' I was surprised. 'I didn't think he had any friends.'

'Well, he has. If you can call them that. They helped him escape. He was seen in a car with two men shortly after he went missing.'

That was about all he could tell me. We spent a few more minutes in the bar and I bought him another drink but he said nothing that might have helped me find his former prisoner.

The business of Powlyn's friends puzzled me. I couldn't figure out who might risk helping him escape after fourteen years. It didn't make sense. Before we parted, the warden gave me the number of Powlyn's solicitor and his psychiatrist.

Outside, the enormous sky was heavy and ominous, with clouds like anvils pressing down on the flat land. From somewhere out in the wetlands beyond the village came the sharp, plaintive cry of a plover. I headed west, towards where the sun would have been... if there had been any sun. A few miles farther on I stopped in a lay-by and used the car phone.

The voice that answered my first call wasn't local. It was a London accent... at a guess I'd have said south of the river.

'Can I speak to Geoffrey Templeton?'

'He's not here.'

I asked when he would be back. 'Not till late. He's out all day. He's gone to...' the woman paused, '...hang on, he's written it down. Yes, he's gone to Happysburg.' I repeated the name. It sounded like something out of the American Civil War.

The woman said Templeton would be home the following day. I hung up and made another couple of calls. I was luckier with them. Afterwards I drove towards Peterborough, skirting the city on the parkway. In the gloom I could just make out the bulk of the cathedral, way over in the centre of the city.

Beyond Peterborough was the A1 and the road to London. I thought about that for a while... and the pointless mission I was on. In an hour, I thought, I could be back in the city. Then I thought about Ronald Cashman.

I checked into a Post House on the outskirts of Peterborough. Inside it was big and anonymous and could have been anywhere in the world. I liked that.

The morning news said that Powlyn was still on the run. I left the hotel at just after nine, driving east and north through yet more flatlands. It was a better day; the sky was dove grey and there was a diffuse smear of sunlight behind the filmy, deliquescent mist draping the fen. Beyond King's Lynn the country started to change; well wooded and with fields that had some camber. I saw road signs to Sandringham and smiled briefly. Templeton was a type who liked to retire close to Royalty.

He lived outside Burnham Market, in a small stone house on a country road. The place looked like the gatehouse of a large country estate. A sign on the creaking gate read, 'The Shooting Lodge.' I smiled again.

I knocked on a dark green wooden door. There was no reply. After another couple of tries I made my way around the back. A metallic blue Range Rover was parked on a patch of land close to the house. The back door was ajar. I knocked and called out a couple of times then gently pushed the door open and stepped inside.

Beyond the tiny kitchen was a small, well appointed room, full of sporting prints and chintzy furniture. It was empty. I heard a noise behind me and turned. Templeton was standing in the doorway. He was carrying a shot-gun.

'I was expecting you.' His voice retained its vigour: a deep, penetrating timbre... an officer's voice.

'So I see.' I nodded at the shot-gun. I noticed it wasn't broken.

He laughed. It was like a bark. 'Well, you never know who else might come calling.' He leaned the shot-gun against the wall. Close enough for him to reach – if he had to.

'Retirement suits you,' I said. 'You look very fit.' He did too. The bastard.

He was about fifty-five. He'd retired from some high-powered job in Five only months before and had returned to north Norfolk to wait for his K or his gong or whatever his type got after a lifetime of dirty service. In the meantime his face had become tanned and his body lean and hard from all the hunting and shooting. His hair, though whiter than when I'd last seen him, was still thick. He was eight years older than me, and looked ten years younger.

'It's living in the country, old boy.' I hated being called that. 'You should try it. Do you good. Plenty of hedging and ditching. Soon get you in shape.'

'No thanks.'

He let out another barking laugh. 'You don't know what you're missing. This is one of the best parts of England. Absolutely filled with history. Nelson was born just up the road, you know.'

I eyed him. 'Yeah? Nelson who?'

His face changed. 'I take it you've come about your escaped murderer?' His voice was suddenly hard-edged.

'Why else? I said I'd come. I spoke to someone yesterday.'

He nodded. 'My cleaning lady. She left a note. Well...' he moved farther into the room '...you've had a wasted journey. I haven't taken any interest in Powlyn or the Cashman murder since the trial. All I know is what I've seen on the news.' He eyed me. 'Are you still working for the father?'

'Yes.'

'For God's sake. Doesn't he realise what he'd find if he discovered her? What she'd look like after fourteen years in the ground? He's better off not knowing.'

'Maybe. But it's important to him. He wants to find her before he dies. Bury her properly.'

He shook his head. 'And you're assisting with this insanity? It's a hell of a bloody way to earn a living. Even for someone like you. You ought to give it up. After all, you must have screwed enough money out of the old man by now.' I stared at him but said nothing. He gave me a cold, supercilious smile. 'You should have stayed in the Corps. You might have been an officer by now.'

I laughed briefly. 'It's because they offered me a commission I left. Sergeant was good enough.' He grunted. After a moment I said, 'Powlyn still denies your testimony. That you saw him with Maxine before she was killed.'

'Well, he would wouldn't he? After all, if he's trying to get a retrial he has to rubbish the evidence that got him convicted.'

I frowned. 'How did you know about that? I didn't know about any retrial until yesterday.'

He gave me another of his supercilious smiles. 'It was on the news, old boy.'

'I didn't see it.'

'The *radio* news. Much better than television.'

'If you say so.' There was another moment's silence. I stared at him. He stared back. 'So you don't know anything about Powlyn or his escape.'

He shook his head. 'Not a thing.'

'But doesn't it strike you as odd that, just when he's got a chance of a retrial, he goes over the wall?'

Templeton made a face like there was a dirty smell under his nose. 'The man's a drug runner and a murderer. A psychotic who brutally murdered a young woman and then buried her God knows where. Who knows why somebody like that does anything? Not even his psychiatrist will know. If I were you I'd give it up. You're never going to find her – and you'll probably never find *him* either.'

I shook my head. 'No, the police will find him soon enough. I'm surprised they haven't got him already. He's been inside too long. He can't last on the outside.'

Templeton grunted.

I left a couple of minutes later. I'd come a long way for nothing... for less than five minutes' conversation with ex-major Geoffrey Templeton. It had got me absolutely no further in finding out where Powlyn might have gone.

Or why.

My next meeting was in Cambridge. I headed south. For the first time in twenty-four hours I was going in the right direction. On either side of the road the flat fen fields stretched into the featureless distance like a prairie. It was eerie... all that land and not a pavement anywhere.

I got to Cambridge. As always it was cycle city, with thousands of students flying about on bicycles, as dumb and unconscious as bullets in a battle. It was called a city but to me it was no more than a small town – a small town in Ruritania, full of cobblestones, cramped narrow streets and medieval college buildings. Parts of it looked like a Disney film set.

I queued for twenty minutes to get a space in a multi-storey before walking to the college. I followed the instructions I'd taken over the phone – through Great Court, into New Court, turn right into Nevile's Court. I found the doorway and walked up a late-Georgian wood-panelled staircase. The centre of each wooden stair had been worn saucer-shaped by years of use. I knocked on a door at the top of the staircase. A voice said, 'Come in.'

He was tall, thin and bald, with a purple bow tie and long, skeletal fingers. The room had more books than I'd ever seen in one place before. Every wall, from top to bottom, was covered by them and there were untidy heaps on the sills of the diamond-mullioned windows. A lot of thick heavy tomes, looking like burned-out tree stumps, were piled in low stacks over the floor. We shook hands. It was like grasping cold spaghetti.

'Sit down.' He moved a stack of books off a well-worn easy chair and put them on the floor. He was lucky to find room.

I sat down. 'Thanks for seeing me.'

He shrugged his narrow shoulders. 'I must admit to some sympathy for the victim's father. In fact' – he gave me a keen look – 'I would be quite interested to meet him. That kind of extended obsession is fascinating. It would make an excellent case study.' He smacked his lips together as if contemplating a feast at high table.

Now I knew why the old buzzard had agreed to meet me. I appraised him. He looked slightly mad. He probably was. In my business I'd learned that a tendency to insanity was a primary requirement for anyone practising psychiatry. And the man opposite me was one of the country's leading practitioners.

'However,' he went on, 'I thought it best for us to meet here, in college, rather than at the department or the hospital.' He gave me the benefit of what I thought was a smile. It made him look as if he had wind. 'As a matter of fact I'm not entirely sure that I should be talking to you at all, and of course you realise that I cannot tell you anything about Mr Powlyn's treatment.'

'Sure. I just want anything you *can* tell me. General stuff.

39

He'd agreed to a new kind of treatment, hadn't he?'

He nodded. 'He'd always refused before, but we've developed a new theory of deep regression... total evocation. It enabled him to cut through the haze of the drugs and to remember *exactly* what happened that night.' He paused and again fixed me with his bird-like stare. 'I'm convinced he didn't kill that girl, you know.'

'So what *did* happen?'

'What he said at his trial. Only now he can recall a lot more detail.'

'Such as?'

'I'm sorry I can't tell you that. If there's a retrial, it will come out then.'

I sighed. Another wasted journey. I tried pumping him for more but he wasn't having any. After a while I made ready to leave. He accompanied me to the top of the staircase.

'There is one thing I can tell you,' he said as I shook his clammy hand. 'I don't think it'll do any harm. During our last session, Mr Powlyn suddenly remembered he'd been driven through Hazebrough that night.'

'Hazebrough?'

'A small village on the coast. South of Cromer.'

I frowned. I'd never heard of it. Powlyn had certainly never mentioned it when I'd seen him in prison. I wondered if it was significant.

I had one more place to go. I got out of Cambridge, picked up the A11 north of Newmarket and headed north-east for Norwich. It was the wrong direction, but at least it would be my last. The news on the car radio announced that Powlyn was still free.

The road bypassed Thetford, slicing between thick, dark-pine plantations. This was Breckland. Cashman had done a lot of digging hereabouts... taking his shovel deep into the woods to excavate the sandy soil in the appalling hope of exhuming what remained of his murdered daughter.

Beyond Snetterton I stopped at a Little Chef and had coffee. I consulted a road map but couldn't find Hazebrough anywhere. I figured it had to be a very small village.

Norwich was scarcely more of a city than Cambridge. It was bigger but still provincial. I stopped to ask directions and had trouble understanding the old guy who finally made me realise the place I wanted was close to Tombland.

Tombland. What a name. It exactly matched my mood and my mission and unerringly described the melancholy country through which I had been chasing a wild goose for two wasted days.

The offices were close to the west front of the cathedral. A brass plaque on the door announced that a series of names were solicitors. I was shown up to a room on the first floor. It was like any other solicitor's office, untidy and cluttered with files and legal briefs bound in pink ribbon.

Powlyn's solicitor was thin enough to be almost transparent. Her skin had the dull patina of the professional dieter and her jawline was so stark it cast a shadow over her titless chest. She came at me like a swarm of bees.

'There's no way I'm prepared to help you,' she snapped. Her voice was like rending sheet metal. 'I agreed to see you because I want a statement from you.'

'A statement from *me?*'

'Certainly. You visited my client a number of times in prison and at no time did he ever change his story that he was innocent. I intend to use that testimony at his retrial.'

'You think there'll be a retrial? Now he's done a runner?'

'Of course. It's foolish of him to escape but that doesn't alter the fact that there's been a serious miscarriage of justice.'

I pulled a face. 'I was hoping you'd have some idea of where he might have gone.'

She shook her head and the long lines of medallions hanging from her earlobes clinked on her shoulders. I watched them, fascinated.

'Even if I knew, which I don't, I wouldn't tell you. You're wasting your time. As my client didn't murder Maxine Cashman it's useless for you to try finding him to ask where she's buried. For all we know, she may not even be dead.'

I sighed. Two days criss-crossing this God-forsaken

countryside to end up getting a hatchet job from a demented ferret. It was no more than I should have expected. 'Well, if you want a statement you know where to find me.' I turned to go. A thought struck me. 'By the way, do you know Hazebrough?'

She looked at me suspiciously. 'Yes. It's on the coast. Why?'

'I hear it's a good place to stay for a weekend. Could you show me. On a map?'

She sighed irritably and pulled an Ordinance Survey from a drawer. 'There.' She stabbed at a place with an emaciated finger. I looked... and swore softly under my breath.

Hazebrough wasn't spelled the way it was said. It was spelled Happisburgh. Like a place out of the American Civil War.

Something caught my eye. I looked closer. Just to the north of Happisburgh was another, even smaller location. Called Ostend.

'Thanks,' I said quietly. I left the office.

Outside, I bought a detailed OS map and made a call from the car. 'Ronald, it's me.'

He was eager to hear my news but I brushed his questions aside.

'Have you been listening to the reports on the radio?' He said he had. 'Has there been any mention of a retrial for Powlyn? A miscarriage of justice and all that?'

'What?' His voice was distraught. 'That can't be right.'

'Has there?'

'No. None. Why, what does it mean?'

I said I'd tell him later and killed the call.

I sat for a few minutes, then dialled the number in Burnham Market. Templeton wasn't there. I left a message on his answering machine. I didn't say a lot... I didn't need to.

Afterwards I drove fast, north out of Norwich and through Wroxham before turning off towards the coast at Stalham. Happisburgh was a moderate-sized village close to the shore, with a lighthouse, a high-spired church and a lot of white-washed bungalows. There was a pub opposite a sharp left turn in the road. I parked the car well out of sight in the car-park.

My map showed a path running along low, sloping cliffs to Ostend. I took a pair of night glasses out of the glove compartment and made my way along the path. It was a little over a mile and I made good time. The light was fading as I reached Ostend.

The place was bleak – just a few rows of wooden chalets, looking like a cross between Butlins and an army camp, set on an apron of concrete. Beyond them was the quietly shifting sea: grey and cold and ominous. The place appeared deserted. I guessed the chalets were used as holiday homes in the summer.

Ostend. I thought about it. Wasn't that Dutch or Old German for East End? To me it looked more like the end of the world.

Close to the cliff path, just this side of the lonely, windswept collection of huts was a radio mast. I hunkered down behind a knoll close to it and waited. The place was desolate. And cold. Nothing moved, except the sea and the wind moaning in the girders of the mast.

I waited two hours, longer than I'd expected. It grew dark and half a moon began faintly to dapple the sea.

At last the lights of a vehicle appeared on the single track leading off the main road a mile away. Through the night glasses I made out a Range Rover. It stopped close to one of the wooden chalets and two men got out. Two. Now I knew why Templeton had taken so long to arrive. He'd got help. I watched him unlock the door to one of the chalets and a dull light come on. His companion stayed close to the vehicle.

I took off a shoe, pulled off one of my socks and loaded it with a couple of heavy pebbles. I wormed my way down the dark, grassy hillock towards the Range Rover.

He was a young guy and whoever had trained him had done a bad job. He stayed in one place, watching the road from where he would expect a car to appear. He had his back to me. I snaked in close to the Range Rover, waited a moment for the moon to move behind a heavy bank of cloud, then moved up swiftly and swung the loaded sock into the base of his skull. I caught him as he crumpled. I felt inside his leather jacket. He was carrying. I pulled the weapon out. It was a Glock – which meant the guy was probably official. I yanked off his trouser belt, turned him on to his face and tied his hands behind his back. I slipped the Glock into my coat pocket.

I straightened up, moved quickly to the chalet into which Templeton had disappeared, crashed open the door and barged straight into a sparsely furnished room. Templeton spun round. The shot-gun he had carried with him into the building lay on a table. I got to it first.

'These things cause accidents,' I announced. I broke the weapon, ejected two cartridges on to the wooden floor and dumped the gun in a corner of the room.

The startled look on Templeton's face disappeared. His voice, as always, was supremely self-assured. 'My man outside?'

'Having a snooze.'

He grimaced. 'You just can't get good people these days. Not like our day, eh?'

I wasn't there for a stroll down Memory Lane. 'You killed Maxine, didn't you?'

He stared at me, then shook his head. 'Not me personally.'

'One of your people, then.'

He was silent for a moment then he shrugged. 'It was a shambles, I'm afraid. We'd found out that Maxine was passing secret NATO data to the other side. The idea was to grab her, interrogate her and then, if we could, turn her. Make her a double agent. We made our move outside Harwich, only it went wrong. Maxine resisted, one of my people got over-excited and she was shot. Naturally we didn't want the other side to know we were on to them, but it was going to be difficult persuading anyone that she'd had an accident with a bullet hole in her head. The other side was bound to be suspicious.'

'So you decided to make her disappear?'

He nodded. 'But it had to be believable, something the other side would accept as genuine, something that wouldn't make them close their operation down. We came up with a scheme to make it appear as if she'd been murdered and her body buried somewhere.'

'All you needed was some poor dumb bastard like Powlyn to stitch up – and see him do life for it.'

He waved a dismissive hand. 'Powlyn was a nasty little drug runner. He didn't matter... not when it was a question of national security.' He must have caught the look on my face. 'Come on, old boy, it was a bloody good scheme. We only had a few hours to put it together – to plant the evidence, pump Powlyn full of heroin, run his car all over East Anglia...'

'...bury Maxine,' I added bleakly.

His face changed. 'That too.' He was silent. 'But the point is,' he went on, 'it worked. The other side bought the story. They never knew we'd sussed Maxine and their operation. We were able to monitor them for years.'

I wasn't interested in stories of successful espionage. 'I take it you've disposed of Powlyn too,' I said. I could hear my voice grating.

He nodded. 'Had to. He was getting good psychiatric help, remembering a lot more of what had gone on. And his bloody lawyer was pushing for a retrial. We couldn't allow what happened to come out.'

'Why the hell not? What difference would it make now? No one's spying on NATO any more. They all want to be part of it.'

He gave me a pitying look. 'God, even you must see what it would do if it came out. What do you think the press would make of it? We have to preserve the integrity of the service.'

'So Powlyn didn't escape. You kidnapped him.'

'Easy enough to do when he was in the rehab unit. No one saw us and he was too surprised to put up any resistance.'

I frowned. 'But why bring him here?'

'How do you know that I did?'

'Your housekeeper told me that you'd gone to Happisburgh. It's only down the road.'

'Is that what put you on to me?'

'That, and the fact that for someone who hadn't followed the case for fourteen years you had a lot of up-to-date information.'

He smiled bleakly. 'You always were brighter than you looked.'

We stared at each other across the bare, soulless room. Then it hit me.

'You brought him here to bury him. You killed him, then brought the body here.' Templeton didn't reply but I could tell from his face that I was right. 'And the reason you did that is because this is where you buried Maxine.'

He gave me a cold stare. 'There's no way you could know that.'

'Sure I know it. You're a traditionalist. If it works once, it'll work again. That's the way you are. You've buried them both here. I'll bet they're not yards apart.'

His face betrayed the truth.

'Where?' I asked quietly.

'What good would it do you to know?'

'Where?' I repeated.

He looked at me clinically. Then he shrugged. 'I suppose it doesn't really matter if you know. You can't do anything about it. In the end you're still one of us.' He paused, then said quietly, 'Not far from the radio mast.'

It occurred to me I might have been sitting on Maxine's grave whilst I was watching the chalet.

'But I would remind you that you have signed the Official Secrets Act,' Templeton continued in his officious voice, 'and as Maxine Cashman is an official secret, I don't need to tell you that you cannot use that information.'

'To hell with that. Ronald Cashman wants his daughter back. He needs to bury her decently. With dignity. I'm going to see that he does. So I'd advise you not to try to stop me.'

'I wouldn't dream of it, old boy.' He said it with a smile... a smile that told me he was going to kill me. If he could.

46

I backed slowly out of the room and the chalet and moved close to the dark bulk of the Range Rover. I took the Glock from my pocket and waited. The next move was up to Templeton.

He came out of the doorway fast, with the shot-gun at high port. He'd forgotten his training. The chalet's dim light was behind him. He saw me and levelled the gun. I fired twice. The bullets crashed him against the door frame and he went down. I didn't bother with him after that. I knew he was dead. I'd fired the way I'd been trained, the only way I knew how... one in the head... one in the heart. I wondered vaguely whether they dished out posthumous gongs to the likes of Templeton.

The guy by the Range Rover was coming round. I hit him hard behind the ear to put him out for a while longer, wiped the Glock clean of prints and put it back inside the leather holster under his jacket. He would have some explaining to do.

So would I. Sooner or later some super spooks would come calling. But by then Maxine and Powlyn's bodies would have been discovered and the spooks would be terrified in case someone made a connection. They'd wonder what I knew but they'd never be sure. It would be too dangerous to kill me... I might have written it all down.

I walked up past the radio mast... past Maxine Cashman's lonely, unknown grave.

Tonight, I thought, I'd make some calls and tomorrow the police would start digging. At least Robert Cashman would be spared the nightmare of unearthing his daughter's body. I was glad about that.

I moved as fast as I could along the cliff path towards Happisburgh. From somewhere in the starlit dark on my left came the ageless sound of the sea crashing on the shore. My sockless foot felt cold but at least now I was moving in the right direction. South. Away from Ostend... away from the forlorn, desolate place that for Maxine and Bobby Powlyn had become a dead end.

A long way farther south was the city... the thousand

square miles of flesh and stone. I was glad to be going back. It was where I belonged.

The Inside Man

Clare Dawson

Clare Dawson was born and raised in a Wiltshire also began writing short fiction. The non-fiction may coexist chance in her time and she has twice valid... times agreeable fiction published series of non-fiction. A short radio play...
first was written to handle and he and he just devel... published in 1970. Clare thinks may be that ever came to realise no romantic fiction, she yet to be sold/achieve...

Clare Dawson was born and raised in Worcester and began writing at an early age. She won two literary competitions in her late teens and has had a wide variety of articles and short stories published in the UK and abroad. A short radio play of hers was broadcast in the late 70s and her first novel was published in 1979. She is currently working on a new crime novel and on romantic fiction. She lives in Cambridgeshire.

'**What did you do** with the body, Barney?'

'What body, Mr Evans?'

'Don't play silly buggers with me, lad. Toby Davenport's body – who else?'

'Don't know nuthin' about that, Mr Evans.'

'If you don't know nuthin',' his interrogator snapped, mimicking the young villain sarcastically, 'you must know something.'

Barney grinned, flashing large uneven teeth. His eyes, small and coal-black, met those of the detective with barely concealed insolence.

'Can't 'elp it if I 'ad lousy teachers at school who couldn't learn me nuthin', can I?'

Detective Chief Inspector Clem Evans left his chair and paced the small interview room, glad to stretch his long legs and let Chris Farley take over. But he studied the younger man as his colleague tried to get a positive response. It was never easy with Terry Barnwell – Barney to all who knew him.

And they knew him well.

A persistent teenage offender, he had finally been jailed at the age of twenty for his part in a betting shop raid. When he came out, after eighteen months, he had surprised everyone – particularly his long-suffering mother – by keeping well away from his old mates, finding himself a steady job and going straight... until the robbery at Toby's jewellers in Ipswich two years later, that is.

He'd done a three-year stretch for his involvement in that and now, released four months ago, he was back on their patch.

As far as Evans and Farley were concerned, Barney was bad news.

Returning to the table, Evans lowered his fourteen-stone frame into the vacant chair and settled his ice-cool gaze on the young man opposite.

Over the years, Barney hadn't changed much.

Still handsome in a roguish kind of way. Still sporting a neatly-trimmed beard and moustache which, combined, managed to prematurely age him and belie his twenty-seven years. Thin-lipped, he had a square jaw and thick neck with a protruding Adam's apple. The dark hair, sleeked back behind his large ears, was collar-length and Evans noticed that he still wore that small silver crucifix in his left ear-lobe, which the policeman had always considered faintly blasphemous for someone of Barney's ilk.

'What you are telling us, then,' Evans began again, 'is that Toby Davenport not only bought you a couple of drinks in the pub that night, but he chatted away to you like an old pal?'

'Yeah.'

'I don't believe you, Barney.'

'It's the truth, Mr Evans. Straight up. There weren't no aggro between us.' Barney stabbed his half-smoked cigarette into the ashtray. 'Toby's a good bloke. He don't 'old no grudges.'

Detective Sergeant Farley butted in.

'The Fiddler's Arms isn't on your patch. Plenty of pubs between your place and the Fiddler's, so what were you doing there?'

'I told yer—'

'Well, tell us again!'

'I was meeting me mate, Steve Jackson. We was planning to do a bit of fishin' together and he knew a good place—'

'Where?' interrupted Evans, adding swiftly, 'And don't say the bloody river, lad, or you'll push my patience too far.'

Barney grinned again. Clearly the senior officer's irritation was amusing him.

'Scotland, Mr Evans. Some place near Dumfries. But Steve told you all this 'imself-'

'What did you do after you left the Fiddler's Arms that night?'

It was Farley who spoke now and Barney scowled at the

burly fair-haired detective, tossing his head back and sniffing. The small crucifix swung dizzily from his ear-lobe.

'Like I keep tellin' yer, we left around eight and I gave Steve a lift back to his gaff. Then I went 'ome to me mum's place in the centre of town.'

'And she was out when you got there?'

'Yeah – at the bingo.'

'Which means she can't confirm what time you got home, can she? Neither could any of the neighbours, as it happens.'

'Farley was remembering the tedious, time-consuming door-to-door enquiries made by junior detectives around Barney's home, which had proven fruitless. Nobody on that council estate was going to help the police.

'The barman said Toby didn't leave till well past ten o'clock. You had plenty of time to nip back after dropping off your friend,' said Evans.

'Why'd I wanna do that?'

'You tell us,' said Farley.

'Well, I never. And you ain't got no proof that I did, neither.'

For the first time, Barney looked ill-at-ease and glared angrily at his two interrogators. Evans switched off the tape recorder, after noting the time and those present, and nodded to the uniformed officer near the door. Barney sprang to his feet, a pained expression on his pale face.

''Ow much longer you goin; to keep me 'ere, Mr Evans? I know me rights. You can't 'old me—'

'I know how long I can hold you, Barney, but a bit longer in the cells won't do you any harm. Give you time to think. See if you can remember anything else you'd like to tell us.'

Evans returned to his office and Farley followed.

'I'll have to let the young sod go soon,' Evans said wearily, staring out of the window at the traffic in the street below. 'We've got nothing on him and he knows it. But I'm just not convinced, Chris. It's too much of a coincidence, his being one of the last people to see Toby Davenport before the man walked out of that bloody pub and vanished! It's been three weeks and not a word from him – not even to his wife.'

Mention of Rachel Davenport brought an instant smile to Farley's lips as he visualised the small, blonde, beautifully-proportioned female they had interviewed at her husband's mini-mansion a couple of miles outside Ipswich. At twenty-five, Rachel was a stunner.

Her marriage to the rich and successful diamond dealer, eighteen years her senior, appeared to be completely happy. Everyone they spoke to confirmed it. The couple had been wed for four years and had a two-year-old son.

Her distress and anxiety since Toby's mysterious disappearance was genuine enough, and Farley had had to amend his cynical view of bimbos who married rich older men. Maybe it *did* work sometimes, he conceded.

'Can't say we haven't checked and double-checked, sir,' he said now, forcing his thoughts back to the discussion in hand. 'No money troubles. No business rivals after his blood. Certainly nothing wrong with his marriage.'

'Nothing wrong healthwise either,' said Evans. 'There could have been some illness he'd chosen to conceal from his wife. Something terminal. A possible motive for suicide, maybe. But nothing. According to his GP, he was a very fit man.'

'It's bloody annoying that none of the photos we circulated in the press and on the telly have brought any response. If he's out there, somebody should have seen him by now.'

'Lord Lucan all over again,' murmured Evans, moving to his desk. 'The wife's adamant he'd never take off like that. It's totally out of character. She's convinced he's dead. And with suicide ruled out, it's got to be murder.'

with suicide ruled out, it's got to be murder.'

'And with Barney being the only one likely to bear a grudge against her husband, she's pointing a finger at him.'

'Maybe. But we need evidence. His alibi is weak all right, but we can't prove he's lying, can we?'

Evans began pacing again, thinking aloud. Farley had the wisdom not to interrupt.

'We know Toby left the pub around half past ten that night. We know he was seen getting into his Merc by a customer leaving at the same time. He was definitely alone. Several witnesses, including the barman, confirm that he was relaxed and cheerful and not drinking too much. And he didn't seem too bothered that the friend he was supposed to be meeting there, didn't turn up.'

'That was the bloke whose car broke down on the motorway, of course.'

'Yes. We also know that Barney's claim that he met Toby by accident in the pub, has been borne out by the barman who also confirmed there was no aggro between the two men. Barney and his pal definitely left around eight o'clock and nobody saw either of them again that night. Witnesses verified what time Steve got home but we've no one to confirm Barney got back to his mum's soon after.'

Evans paused, passing a large spatula-shaped hand over his clean-shaven face and plucking at his thick eyebrows, absently.

'Toby's Mercedes was still in the pub car-park next morning and all the following day, until the publican spotted it and called us. It was securely locked. The scenes-of-crime officer found nothing either. The Merc was as clean as a whistle, inside and out, apart from Toby's prints and Rachel's. Yet what puzzles me, Chris, is that the customer who was leaving at the same time as Toby, *swears* he saw Toby get into his car. So why did he change his mind? And

Farley went off to get some coffee, leaving his boss to reflect on the businessman who'd started out with one small jewellery shop in Lowestoft and now, twelve years later, had a string of them all across East Anglia. Evans knew that Toby was wedded to his work and, apart from one long-time mistress who had eventually deserted him for another man, the jeweller had seemed destined to remain a bachelor... until Rachel came along.

Farley returned with two mugs of coffee and a question on his lips.

'Do you really believe Toby is as forgiving as Barney says he is, guv?'

'Yes, I do. He's never been known as a hard man, despite his success in business. And he's always been proud of the fact that he'd given the lad a job, despite his criminal record, and that Barney had repaid him over the next two years by doing well and keeping out of trouble. For a while, he almost had *us* convinced that the lad was a reformed character. Barney had a good future ahead of him. He was a bloody fool to throw it all away.'

'And all because of Rachel.'

'So he said. But no one could attach any blame to the girl for what happened. It was common knowledge that Barney was besotted, but we know from the staff that Rachel never encouraged him. Far from it. He'd started pestering her almost from the day she started working there – about a month before the robbery, in fact. He simply wouldn't take no for an answer.'

'Then he got it into his head that lavishing gifts and costly holidays on her would win her over – hence his part in the raid on the shop.'

'He was a fool to do it for a measly five grand, when the Cartwright brothers got away with thirty thousand quid's worth of top quality diamonds,' said Evans, contemptuously. 'But it was patently obvious they must have known in advance that the gems would be in the safe that day. Only the shop staff knew that a dealer from Antwerp was flying in that afternoon. That meant an inside man and Barney was the obvious suspect. Admittedly, he had a good alibi but when Toby alerted us to a flaw in Barney's story, we'd got him. Naturally he grassed on the Cartwrights to get himself a reduced sentence.'

'Barney must have had one hell of a shock when he came out of jail and found that Rachel had married Toby,' said Farley, stirring his coffee briskly. 'I don't believe he's accepted it as calmly as he makes out. I think he's hopping mad. And he already hates Toby for shopping him.'

'Except Toby didn't, did he? It was Rachel who was smart enough to catch Barney out in a lie and spot the flaw in his alibi. It was she who told her boss and then he told us. Barney never knew.'

'Maybe he'd have felt differently about her, if he had.'

'Who knows? His sort of obsession defies logic.'

Farley, collecting up the empty mugs, voiced another thought.

'If Toby *is* dead, guv, could Barney have done it? I mean, he's a bad lot and all that, but there's no GBH on his records—'

'Take another look at them, Chris,' Evans responded. 'Eight years ago, Barney was involved in a pub fight. And *that* was over a girl. According to witnesses, he went berserk and almost throttled the other lad. If the other customers hadn't pulled him off, he'd have been facing a manslaughter charge. He's got it in him, all right.'

The telephone rang, and as Evans lifted the receiver he added, 'We've got that television programme tomorrow, remember. That might bring some results. In the meantime, nip down to the cells and show Barney the door, will you?'

After the *Crimewatch UK* programme on television, Evans felt the stirrings of optimism. With phone calls streaming in from people claiming to have seen the missing businessman, and officers all over the country following up the claims, hopes had run high for several weeks. But by the end of a second hectic week Davenport was still a missing person.

Evans got into work the following morning feeling despondent and more than a little irritated by their lack of success. When Rachel Davenport telephoned him, shortly after he got in, he was surprised to find her agitated and reluctant to say too much over the phone. He agreed to call at the house and rang off.

When he arrived, Rachel Davenport – elegant as ever in a black and white suit and stylish shoes – looked pale and was clearly upset. When he left half an hour later, however, Evans was in a happier frame of mind.

'There's been an interesting development, sir,' Farley greeted him when he got back. 'Our surveillance lads say that Barney's been paying regular visits to Mrs Davenport. Turning up with flowers and the like.'

'I know. She told me. He's almost a daily visitor. But she's no fool. If Toby *is* dead, that makes her a very rich widow. Her first instinct was to tell him to bugger off but, as her husband bore no grudge, she felt she should at least be civil to him. Just as well, as it happens. Anyway, she's come up with some surprising information, Chris. Sit down and I'll tell you all about it.'

On Tuesday morning, facing his team in the briefing room, Evans completed what he had to say in his usual concise manner and, as his officers left to carry out their instructions, he returned to his office. Concentration on work was difficult. Rachel Davenport kept drifting into his thoughts and he couldn't deny a sneaking admiration for the woman's intuitive mind and cool resolve.

The day dragged. By evening he was pacing his office. Impatient. Irritated. At ten o'clock, he was already thinking of home and a hot bath when the phone rang. Minutes later he was outside and heading for his car, Chris Farley at his side.

The police surveillance car outside Barney's home was already on the move, tailing the villain's car with practised skill. Evans, in radio contact with the men driving the unmarked police cars, knew when one of them dropped out it would be succeeded by another and concentrated on the route being conveyed back to him. Farley said nothing but shared his senior officer's excitement.

Barney was heading towards London. After a few miles Evans found himself behind the unmarked police car between himself and Barney and when it pulled into a lay-by he took over, keeping the Vauxhall in his sights as it turned off the busy motorway and headed inland.

In the pale moonlight, Evans became aware of dark fields to the left and a wooded area on the right which seemed to become denser as the miles passed.

Presently Barney slowed down, turned into a narrow gap between the hedgerows and headed into the woods beyond. Evans followed slowly and cautiously, using his side-lights only, and stopping when he saw the Vauxhall halt just ahead of him. He switched off the engine and lights, and watched as Barney locked his car and set off into the woods.

Aware that back-up was close behind them, Evans and Farley followed. When they emerged from the trees, they were only yards away from a large, derelict farmhouse. Even in the poor light, they could see several buildings nearby in an advanced state of decay and, as they came up to the tall perimeter fence, spotted the demolition notice and the warning to the public to keep out.

But their quarry was already through a hole in the fence, heading for a barn on the left. Seconds later he'd disappeared from view.

Several officers had moved silently into strategic positions around the barn as Evans and Farley moved closer. Through a crack in the rotting wooden door, they saw Barney, spade in hand, busily digging in one corner. A torch was on the ground near his feet.

They waited. The minutes ticked inexorably by.

At last the sound of digging stopped. When they moved in, Barney was on his knees, searching for something in the crude grave. And for once, when he saw them, Terry Barnwell's insolent grin was noticeably absent.

'Barney was always a fool,' Rachel Davenport said bitterly as she faced the two detectives some days later. 'I could tell him anything and he'd believe it.'

'Well, the lie about your husband's body-belt certainly fooled him,' said Farley.

'It wasn't entirely a lie,' she explained. 'Toby did have some body-belts specially designed and made for him. He always wore them close to the skin and they were undetectable. I know it seems stupid to carry gems around like that but sometimes Toby had to, and the belt was safer than any attaché case.'

'Only that night – the night he disappeared – he wasn't wearing one,' commented Evans.

'No.' Rachel shook her head and Farley, watching her, noticed with pleasure the way her soft blonde curls bobbed ever so slightly as she did so. 'Barney didn't know that, of course. When I spun him that yarn about Toby carrying all those gems in his belt that night and how scared I was that he had been murdered for them, I could see he was taking it all in. I could almost sense his excitement.' A hint of anger crept into her voice suddenly. 'He even believed me when I said Toby was doing a cash deal to dodge tax. Barney, better than anyone, should have remembered that Toby wasn't bent!'

'Just as well he didn't, Mrs Davenport,' said Evans,

getting up to leave. 'If he had, he'd never have gone back to the body to try to recover the gems.'

Later, in the car, Farley said, 'I'm still a bit puzzled, sir. How did Rachel know for sure that Barney had killed her husband?'

'Music, Chris. Country and Western music.'

'So?'

'Toby was an opera lover and everybody who worked for him, knew it – including Barney. What he didn't know was that, while he was enjoying Her Majesty's hospitality in Pentonville, his ex-boss had developed a taste for Country and Western music. Toby kept a lot of the cassettes in his Merc. So, when Barney let it slip that he'd been surprised by the music, Rachel knew immediately that he couldn't have known about it, unless he'd been inside the Mercedes, or near it, when the tape was playing. That meant he had to have been in the car-park that night when Toby left the pub. She said Barney actually named the tune and the singer!'

'Must have given her a nasty shock.'

'Yes, but luckily she had the presence of mind not to show it. It was unlikely, too, in the short time he and Barney were chatting, that Toby would have mentioned his new interest. Even if he had, he wouldn't have told Barney which tape he had in his car that night.'

'And we know now that he parked on the far side of the car-park, alongside the Merc which more or less concealed the Vauxhall, and kept out of sight until the other customers had driven off. Then he ordered Toby out of his car at gunpoint, using a replica gun, hit him over the head, strangled him and then dumped the body in the boot of the Vauxhall. He locked up the Merc, taking care not to leave any prints behind, and then drove around for a while trying to decide what to do with the body.'

'And he chose that derelict barn because he'd seen it on one of his fishing trips. The river wasn't far away.'

'Heavy rain that night got rid of any blood near the Merc,

but the scenes-of-crime lads found some in Barney's car boot, despite his having thoroughly cleaned it. They don't miss much.'

'And it was an opportunist killing, guv?'

'Barney's admitted it. When he saw Toby on his own in the Fiddler's Arms, he saw his chance. And he might have got away with it, if Rachel hadn't been as smart this time as she was before. If Barney had known, I reckon he would have been a lot less trusting.'

'I can't help feeling sorry for her,' said Farley, his thoughts on the grieving widow in her mini-mansion.

Evans glanced at the young bachelor and grinned mischievously. 'You won't be the only one, I'm sure,' he said. 'But from what she was telling me, I think her young son will become the centre of her life from now on... at least, for the next few years.'

Dodgy, Very

James Melville

James Melville, author of over twenty books, many short stories and articles, became a full-time writer and reviewer in 1983 after a long career overseas as a cultural diplomat. Best known as the creator of Japanese police superintendent Otani, Melville has a new hero, Ben Lazenby, in his latest novel *Diplomatic Baggage,* set in Hungary.

'**Dodgy?** How do you mean, dodgy?'

Francis, sixth Earl of Cringleford, was still under forty, and although he had enjoyed a sheltered childhood it had been followed by a bruising adolescence at Eton. It was preposterous to suppose that he might never before have heard the word, but all the same his uncertain tone gave the impression that he was putting inverted commas round it.

'Come now,' Osbert Parsley said indulgently, 'you know perfectly well what I'm driving at. It's an entirely feasible scheme that should make us a bob or two.'

He lowered his voice before continuing. 'In fact, between ourselves, we're talking telephone numbers, so obviously it'll mean bending the rules just a trifle. Did I tell you about the sweet deal I put together over the Monet just before the bottom fell out of the Impressionist market? It was a breeze, and old Hashimoto was delighted with my efforts.'

'Was he.'

Parsley appeared not to notice the lack of enthusiasm in Cringleford's voice. 'He was indeed. I tell you, Francis, there's no jiggery-pokery really serious collectors won't lend themselves to once they've got their eye on something they want. And the Japanese are particularly ruthless, especially when they have dubious connections. Did you know some of the Corots that went missing from that provincial museum in France about ten years ago turned up in Japan? A gangster boss bought them as a job lot and hung them in his house, to please his wife and impress his underlings.'

'Er, no, I hadn't heard that.'

'Take my word for it, old man. Mind you,' Parsley added with an air of wishing to be fair-minded, 'one has to watch the market carefully and decide when the time's ripe to jump in. That's why I'm suggesting you should do something soon about those Chinese bronzes cluttering up your house. People are turning their attention back to the old and tested collectibles.'

Parsley beamed encouragingly at his companion as he gently swirled the contents of his brandy balloon round. His bland smile sat well on his smoothly-shaven, pink face, and the expensive suit went a long way to disguise his plump body. Parsley had been only a year or two senior to Cringleford at Eton, but had the look of a man pushing fifty.

'I don't come here very often, you know,' he added inconsequentially, looking round the huge room with its lofty ceiling. To anybody familiar with the world of London clubs the remark would have been otiose. For Parsley gave off a whiff of decadence; an artistic, faintly louche impression that one might expect to emanate from habitués of the Savile in Mayfair rather than from those of the great and good who frequent the Athenaeum.

Nobody could possibly have taken Parsley for a bishop or a governor of the BBC. He might just have passed for a new-style vice-chancellor: a bland operator at the helm of one of the former polytechnics lately transmogrified by a stroke of the pen into universities, but such are most unlikely to be put up for election, much less approved by the membership committee.

The peer chose to ignore, or more likely failed to register, the last remark. 'Well, I'm sorry to be old-fashioned, but to me there's something in the notion of a national heritage, you know. This sort of thing you're suggesting is an affront to people's pride in their what d' you call it, ancestral past. Dammit, how should we feel if people started spiriting, um, for example' – he looked round for inspiration but found none in the stodgily handsome room – 'well, I don't know a thing about art, but Turners, say, out of the country?'

'Turners! For Christ's sake! You really are as much of a silly ass as you look,' said Parsley, but only to himself. Aloud he said, 'My dear Francis, how the blazes do you imagine your great-grandfather acquired the bronzes in the first place? He was a member of an early diplomatic mission to China, you tell me. So he did what diplomats abroad with an eye for quality have always done: laid his hands on some choice pieces and brought them home with him.'

'Yes, but I've always been given to understand the bronzes were *given* to him, d'you see. As presents.' Cringleford shifted in his seat. 'Well, most of them, anyway,' he added uneasily, drooping in his leather chair and seldom allowing his pale blue eyes to focus on Parsley's beady black ones.

'You know, Francis, if I weren't your guest here I'd invite you to tell that to the marines. As it is, all I ask is that you should think about my idea.'

Some twenty minutes later Osbert Parsley proceeded just a little unsteadily down the stairs of the club and into Waterloo Place. Then he turned left into Pall Mall with the intention of walking the short distance to Old Bond Street. There, and in the neighbouring side streets, are to be found the exclusive little galleries and fine art establishments among whose proprietors he was well known as a freelance appraiser and broker with something of a reputation for unearthing valuable pieces in unlikely places.

The earl was not with him. He had made vague noises while seeing his guest off about popping in to his bank. In fact he couldn't endure Parsley's company a moment longer, and he lingered in the hall until he judged that the odious man was out of sight. Then he set off in the opposite direction, past the National Gallery and along the side of St Martin-in-the-Fields , and stopped in front of the impressive premises of Messrs Coutts & Co., bankers to the Queen and the Earl of Cringleford. There was a bus stop there, at which he could catch a number 28 to Liverpool Street. It seemed absurd to save a taxi fare after standing Parsley a quite expensive lunch at the Athenaeum, but he was accustomed to making small, discreet economies, and had not the slightest desire to pop into his bank: the recollection of his most recent interview with his account manager was painfully vivid.

During the bus ride to the station Francis did think about what Parsley had said, and with a growing awareness that in spite of what had been for him a spirited dismissal of the proposal, he might in the end be driven to sell at least some of the bronzes if he could. It was the logical thing to do. The collection of ancient Chinese artefacts amassed by his great-grandfather the third Earl was, mercifully, not in the least notorious; unlike the Greek marbles ripped from the Parthenon by the seventh Earl of Elgin who, in an act of philanthropy with unfortunate consequences, had presented them to the nation.

The Elgin marbles were now a bone of diplomatic contention, whereas so far as Cringleford was aware, the present Chinese authorities neither knew of the existence of his great-grandfather's collection nor demanded its return. For that matter, hardly anybody outside the family circle *had* ever heard about the Cringleford bronzes, much less seen them. A postgraduate student preparing a Ph.D. thesis on nineteenth-century diplomatic relations between Britain and China had visited the house some six years earlier, but had been so discouraged by the chaotic state of the neglected archives that she had relegated the third Earl to a footnote and omitted any reference to the passionate and scholarly interest in the history of Chinese art that had made him in the late Victorian period a leading expert on the subject.

In his old age the former envoy had become increasingly eccentric, and had frightened the next generation of scholars off. The result had been that the full extent and variety of his acquisitions was unknown to experts a hundred years later. The bronzes were regarded by his ignorant descendants as no more than curios, mementoes of an itinerant diplomatic career to be classed with the assegais, beaten copper trays and the mounted heads of wild animals that had also accumulated in the many nooks and recesses of Brackenheath Hall.

Osbert Parsley had first noticed the dingy bronze vessels lying about the vast ancestral home when, as an adolescent but already accomplished social climber, he used his seniority at Eton to wangle an invitation to spend part of one summer vacation there with Francis, who had already inherited the title. The visit had been abruptly truncated when Parsley was discovered with Francis's younger sister Lady Penelope Bertrand, aged fourteen, in her bedroom. By her mother the dowager Countess, and in the very nick of time, it seems. Parsley had accepted his banishment with good-humoured nonchalance, and took his revenge when a few years later he renewed his acquaintance with Lady Penelope on neutral ground and completed what he had as a schoolboy begun with her enthusiastic co-operation.

Francis had deeply disapproved of the whirlwind affair that ensued, and been pleased when his sister decided to marry another, much more suitable man. By then he had concluded that Osbert Parsley was a cad and a bounder. He was confirmed in his opinion when, after Penelope was married, Parsley had continued to exercise something of a spell over her and, Francis suspected, remained her occasional lover. The marriage failed, as did her next; and two years ago Penelope had, albeit briefly and disastrously, taken Parsley, by then accepted by dealers as a more or less respectable connoisseur of works of art, as her third husband.

This not only resulted in a distinct *froideur* between brother and sister, but also led to Parsley's unwelcome reappearance in Francis's life, as 'one of the family now, old boy'. As long as the marriage survived, the dealer occasionally turned up at Brackenheath Hall uninvited, and was admitted only because his reluctant host was an amiable man who shrank from confrontation. Polly Cringleford refused to stay in the same room as Parsley, and Francis endured his bonhomous reminiscences of what he claimed to have been their inseparable comradeship at Eton as best he could in the hope that he would soon go away.

On one such occasion Parsley had picked up an incense burner covered in verdigris, studied it for a moment, and then asked a few polite questions about its provenance and that of the other bronzes in the house. Cringleford thought little of it at the time, and was unaware that Parsley had noted the paradox that a collection of unknown extent but certainly enormous value was kept virtually disregarded in a house which was in an advanced state of dilapidation. The walls were damp, the wallpaper mildewy and peeling off here and there, and the ceilings crumbling.

Following that visit to the decaying pile in Norfolk, Parsley had elicited certain information from Lady Penelope without her realising it, consulted various well-informed cronies, and then bided his time. It wasn't until some months after Penelope had divorced him and embarked on a fourth matrimonial adventure, this time with a merchant banker, that Parsley had telephoned and, with a great air of mystery, told Cringleford that he had a proposition to put to him.

His former brother-in-law still couldn't fathom the process by which Parsley had gone on to ventriloquise an invitation to lunch at the Athenaeum, of which the peer remained a member although he could barely afford the subscription these days. For the Cringlefords were indeed exceedingly pressed for ready cash. They had let the greater part of their land to local farmers, but even to keep the house ticking over cost vast sums which they didn't have, and to restore it was out of the question unless they gave it to the National Trust. Then there were the children: adorable but expensive to clothe and feed, while the cost of their education didn't bear thinking about.

At Polly's instigation, her husband had a couple of years earlier taken his seat in the House of Lord. He had been astonished to learn that by showing up and signing in when their lordships were sitting, he could claim travelling and generous daily attendance allowances from deferential officials. With many qualms of conscience he had taken to doing this for the sake of reducing his overdraft at the bank, feeling duty bound in return to spend hour after boring hour in the Chamber pretending to take an interest in politics.

As he rode the escalator down to the concourse at Liverpool Street Station, he tried to remember the details of Osbert Parsley's scheme. Telephone numbers, he had said. They kept changing people's telephone numbers these days, but even Cringleford knew that this meant a great deal of money. However, because of something to do with export licences it wasn't just a simple matter of having some of the bronzes valued and then leaving Sotheby's to do the rest. No, it would be necessary to – well, not to put too fine a point on it – *smuggle* them out of England so that they could be 'discovered' in some other country where the political situation was unstable or corrupt, and the bureaucracy amenable to the requirements of international entrepreneurs such as Parsley.

Parsley had talked expansively about possibilities. Lebanon would be ideal, he said wistfully, except that it was a highly improbable source of hitherto undiscovered Chinese antiquities. On the other hand he had excellent Lebanese contacts who were discreetly adept at procuring at a price such useful documents as official certificates of authentication and export permits, and with whom he had dealt to their mutual satisfaction in the past.

Now where might choice Chinese bronzes of the Sung Dynasty reasonably turn up today? The answer had to be somewhere in south-east Asia, where communities of Chinese merchants had resided for centuries. Malaysia was a possibility, but Singapore with its sternly incorruptible government was a no-go area. Indonesia on the other hand was quite promising, and Parsley's Lebanese friends might even have extended family contacts in Jakarta or Surabaya.

Parsley oozed confidence. 'Just make the decision, old boy, and leave all the worrying to me. Even after deducting the various expenses – you won't want to know the sordid details, will you – and my commission, you and Polly'll net more than enough to be able to fix the roof, find school fees and live it up as an earl and countess should.'

Francis ran into the Bishop of Norwich on platform 9. His public duties had brought him into occasional contact with the prelate long before he had begun to attend debates in the House of Lords and encounter him more frequently. They exchanged a few awkward words, Francis blushing furiously before excusing himself and making off towards the rear of the train with head bowed. As he took his first class seat the bishop charitably assumed that the peer was embarrassed because his own ticket was in what the bishop still thought of as third: he had of course heard rumours about the Cringleford family's straitened finances and sympathised, since those of his diocese were also distinctly iffy.

The man of God was wrong. Having been wrestling with his conscience all the way from the Athenaeum and being on the brink of overcoming it, Francis felt that the Almighty was unfairly taking a hand by arranging for His principal legally recognised delegate in the diocese of Norwich to confront him there on the premises of Railtrack. During the journey Francis therefore reviewed the arguments afresh. By the time the train reached Colchester he had concluded that any enterprise Osbert Parsley himself described as 'dodgy' would be bound to involve not only technical illegalities, but actual crime.

At Ipswich he thought for a while about the notion of crime, and told himself that, well, there was crime, and then again, crime. By Stowmarket he felt that there was a big difference between diddling the bureaucrats and doing positive harm to innocent human beings; and as the train pulled out of Diss he was defensively pointing out to himself that, after all, he wouldn't benefit personally from a large financial windfall, except in terms of peace of mind. For he would of course apply the proceeds of the sale of part of his undisputed property to the welfare of his wife and children, and in substantial measure to putting the house into such a condition that it would again be a worthy part of that national heritage he had spoken so protectively about to Parsley.

When the train reached Norwich twenty minutes later and the two men converged on the exit, the bishop was a little startled but gratified to observe that the earl's previously hangdog and sheepish manner had been replaced by a certain jauntiness, and that his affable remarks about the pleasantness of the journey betrayed no lingering embarrassment. Cringleford even accepted the offer of a lift in the bishop's car and quite unashamedly asked to be dropped at Sainsbury's, conveniently near the bus station.

Polly Cringleford was astounded when, having welcomed her husband home to Brackenheath Hall with depressing news – the estimate for treatment of the woodworm in the east wing had been received and was nearly three times higher than they had expected in their own worst-case imaginings – Francis merely smiled seraphically and urged her not to worry.

'I expected you to be suicidal when you heard,' she remarked in a puzzled way. 'Especially as you were so fed up over having to go all the way to London to meet Ghastly Parsley.'

'Oh, he isn't so bad really, you know.'

Polly looked even more bewildered at this, but Francis, who had indeed gone on at some length that morning over his bowl of muesli about the general unsavouriness of the man she referred to by a variety of uncomplimentary epithets, merely went on smiling and kissed her on the cheek.

Later that evening, after the children had gone to bed, Francis said out of the blue, 'You know, darling, I've been thinking.'

'Have you now. What about?'

'The bronze things my great-grandfather brought back with him from China. There are dozens of them and they might be valuable, you know. I think we should get them insured.'

'God, those battered old eyesores? *Insure* them? Don't be ridiculous. Who on earth would want to pinch them? They're hideous, and covered with mould anyway. I was thinking of giving a few to the white elephant stall at the parish fête next month.' Then Polly's eyes glistened and she adopted a conspiratorial manner. 'I *say,* you're not planning to set the place on fire, are you? For the insurance money?' Her eager expression faded as Francis shook his head slowly.

'Nothing like that. Dear Polly, how could you even think I'd do such a thing?'

'Oh dear, I s'pose not. *Noblesse oblige* and all that. Anyway, we'd never get away with it.'

'I thought we might sell some, though. Of the bronzes. Osbert reckons they might be worth a lot.'

'How the hell does *he* know?'

'Say what you like about Osbert—'

'I always do.'

'—but he *is* very knowledgeable, and he's a licensed appraiser, after all. Anyway, I'm going to hunt through Great-Grandfather's papers and see what I can dredge up.'

The insurance people were glad to do business with a peer of the realm, especially when the Earl of Cringleford submitted an itemised list of the bronzes, written out in the third Earl's own impeccable copperplate hand, explaining that he had recently unearthed it in the family archive. The list was accompanied by a signed, scrawled note on a sheet of Mr Osbert Parsley's headed paper to the effect that he valued the collection at £780,000 for insurance purposes. Francis had been tempted to make it a round million, but thought on reflection that the lower figure sounded more convincing. The insurance company's area manager took a photocopy of the list, handing the original reverently back to Francis, and after a day or two confirmed that cover against loss by fire or theft would be provided, on condition only that the bronzes were kept in a secure room under lock and key.

The 'appraisal' had been supplied to Francis by his sister, with whom he had enjoyed a long and confidential conversation. Lady Penelope, a cheery, generous-hearted woman, was delighted to be reconciled with her brother. She was only too pleased to confirm that she had, however belatedly, come to share his lifelong view of the unspeakable Parsley, hinting that it was only during their short marriage that he had revealed his true nature and proclivities to her.

After Francis told her what he had discovered among their great-grandfather's papers and what he proposed to do about it, Penelope not only – with a cat-like smile – produced a few sheets of her former husband's headed writing paper, but also specimens of his handwriting, and proceeded to demonstrate an impressive talent for forgery.

Hew new husband had, in the first flush of connubial bliss, rashly provided her with an American Express Gold Card, and when Francis confessed that he couldn't raise the money for the substantial insurance premium, Penelope provided it. She didn't even ask him for an IOU. In fact it was as though twenty years had disappeared, and they were two gleeful teenagers again.

With Polly's help Francis emptied a long-disused maid's room and, to meet the insurance company's requirements, had it fitted with a brand new security lock. Then they rounded up as many of the bronzes as they could find and stowed them away in what they had christened 'Aladdin's Cave'.

Some weeks later, when Polly and the children were staying with her parents in Northumberland, Osbert Parsley arrived at Brackenheath Hall by appointment late one evening in the capacious Volvo estate car he used for what he described as 'slumming'. It was after sunset, and inside the house with no lights on it was almost dark.

In the gloom Francis led him to the newly adapted store-room and handed him the key. After wrestling with the new and complicated security lock Parsley eventually succeeded in opening the door and entering. With little snorts of greedy enthusiasm he rooted among the bronzes and with the aid of a pencil torch selected seven or eight items which Francis put into plastic bin-liners for him.

'Looking forward to your trip to Jakarta, I expect,' Francis said as Parsley prepared to drive away. 'I do hope it all goes well. I mean, won't it be tricky taking those through Customs there?'

'Don't be naive, Francis. They're going by sea, as part of a consignment of miscellaneous kitchenware to be delivered to my Lebanese friend's cousin. He owns a general store in Surabaya. Take a couple of months, but safe as houses. As soon as I get word they've arrived I'll go by air as a tourist and sort out the details for the next stage.'

'I say, I hope you're not proposing to go first class and charge it to expenses.'

'Really, Francis, for a man who's in line to collect a fortune you can be singularly nit-picking. For heaven's sake trust me, old boy. I trust *my* contacts, after all.'

After Parsley had gone, Francis thoughtfully put on a pair of Sainsbury's disposable gloves and removed most of the remaining items from the strong room. These he heaped anyhow into cardboard boxes and concealed in one of the many attics in the house.

Finally he closed the door and re-locked it. Penelope had been right to point out that patience was a virtue, and that it would be wise to wait until Parsley was on his way to Indonesia before discovering and reporting the theft of the Cringleford Collection. Penelope had read somewhere that fingerprints persist indefinitely if undisturbed, and Parsley had left plenty. So the police would be bound to find some of them on the door and shelves as evidence of an intruder whose prints didn't match those of any member of the Cringleford family.

'Who knows, they might even have Osbert's on file and nab him,' Penelope breathed dreamily as Francis was leaving. 'Oh, Frankie, wouldn't it be super if his Japanese gangster or whoever it is he's selling them to finds out! Dear old Great-Grandfather, I do wish we could have met him.'

'So do I. When I found that letter to him you could have knocked me down with a feather. What a man! A perfectly genuine authority on the subject of Chinese bronzes, but a scholar with a sense of humour. Imagine devoting decades to building up that collection! He should have lived to add Osbert to it.'

Penelope giggled so much that she snorted inelegantly, then wiped tears of laughter from her eyes. 'No, he wouldn't have wanted to collect Osbert. You're forgetting that Great-Grandfather specialised in *clever* fakes.'

Flat Share

Judith Saxton

Judith Saxton was born and brought up in Norwich, moving constantly as a child, working her way out of the city until the family ended up in the village of Blofield, half-way to Great Yarmouth. She and her husband now divide their time between a bungalow in Thorpe St Andrew, a semi-detached house in North Wales and a caravan on the Isle of Anglesey where she does much of her writing.

She has written under several names for different publishers, and recently had published her fiftieth book, which is set partly in Norfolk. She is now struggling to understand the Spanish Civil War for her next book, *Harvest Moon*.

Every other Thursday after work, I have tea with Auntie Ada. It's a habit I started last year, because it was Matthew's late night at the bank and I didn't much fancy going back to an empty flat, and now I enjoy it, and so does Auntie. It's a little oasis of family time, spent together, with both of us relaxed and in harmony.

In winter we have stews and casseroles followed by fruit pie or a crumble. In summer we have something light; soup, a salad, trifle. In winter we sit by the fire, watch Auntie's telly, and talk. In summer we do Auntie's garden, weeding, hoeing, picking beans or peas or digging potatoes, and we talk then as well, naturally.

Then at about a quarter past nine I hop into the car, drive to the bank, and at nine-thirty, when Matthew emerges, he gets into the passenger seat and we drive home together.

Not any more, though, because ten days ago I discovered quite by chance that Matthew, the two-timing rat, had been having a torrid affair with a girl who worked on his counter.

Everything happened fast after that. Matthew and I quarrelled and he packed his bags, tight-lipped and angry that I had dared to expect at least a degree of fidelity from one of God's chosen sex. Then he walked out of the flat and, it later transpired, out of my life. He took his CD player, the put-u-up, his duvet with its scarlet and black striped cover and matching pillowcases, and his yellow alarm clock. He took his clothes, a blue towel with anchors around the hem and my favourite saucepan, the good one with the wooden handle and matching lid. I thought of making him give it back – it cost me a fiver at a car boot sale – but decided not to bother. For one thing I wasn't too sure where he had gone and for another, you never knew, he might see sense and come back. I didn't *want* him exactly, but I was finding the evenings lonely, and though it was bliss spreading myself all over our king-sized bed, I missed both the striped duvet and, if I'm honest, the romps beneath it which we had shared.

So when Thursday came, I said cheerio to Sally and Lou, my particular friends at the office, hopped into my Astra and drove to Auntie's little house on Thorpe Road, just before the railway bridge and almost but not quite opposite The Griffin pub. She opened the door as soon as she heard the car and we grinned at each other.

'Hello, my woman – dinner's on the table. Beef in red wine tonight, an' a spotted dick for afters, bein' as it's a chilly old night.'

It was cold, so we went straight into the lovely warm kitchen and Auntie dished up and as we ate, I told her about Matthew. She's a real love, Auntie is, honest and straightforward but never tactless and never unkind and that, believe me, is rare these days. So by the time we reached the coffee and After Eights (I supply them, a box a fortnight) Auntie was telling me that she had never liked Matthew and certainly never kidded herself that he was good enough for me.

'He were downright selfish, that feller,' she said roundly. 'He come round here a half-dozen times, happy enough to sit an' yarn round the fire, but when you axed him to dig over my 'tater patch... well, allus an excuse. I never seen him exert hisself for someone else, nor I don't 'spec' I never will. You're best off without a feller like that.'

'I know,' I said, 'but it's going to be expensive in the flat by myself as well as lonely. And it isn't everyone who wants to work in Norwich and live in Yarmouth, so it isn't going to be easy to get a new flat-share.'

'No, that it in't,' she agreed. 'Specially since the murder.'

'Murder? What murder?'

We were sitting at the little table in front of her kitchen window and Auntie leaned over and took the *Evening News* off the draining board.

'That murder,' she said, stabbing the front page with a stiffened forefinger. 'Poor gal, drove back home to Yarmouth from somewhere... the paper don't say where... stopped her motor, and the chap pounced. Strangled her sittin' there in the driver's seat.' Auntie tutted disapprovingly. 'What's the world comin' to, that's what I say, when a young gal can't drive out alone of a night time?'

'That's awful,' I agreed, reading the short paragraph at a

glance. 'They haven't caught anyone yet, but they probably will. It's usually someone you know, they say.'

'That's domestics,' Auntie said knowledgeably. 'This in't one o' them. Well, just you keep your eyes peeled, gal, when you're gettin' out o' that motor o' yourn. And by the same token, get a gal to share this time; she'll give a hand wi' the housework, she might even cook. More'n Matthew did, I'll be bound.'

I had never quite got it across to Auntie that Matthew and I weren't just flatmates but an item, a couple. But perhaps I hadn't tried very hard because, when I thought about it, I never envisaged us as a Darby and Joan, silver-haired and smiling on opposite sides of the fireplace. I suppose, subconsciously, I knew it wouldn't last. Anyway it was too late to explain now, with Matthew gone, so I just said I'd put an advert on the board at work and would wait for the replies to flood in. Or even trickle in. Auntie said she'd ask around, and added, did I know that 'her next door' had got a new lodger – a policeman this time. Ever so nice, quite young and definitely unmarried.

'Have you asked him for his spare helmet?' I enquired, and we both giggled; Auntie, a confirmed spinster, had always had a yen for a policeman's helmet to hang in her hallway.

'Good as a feller about the place but a deal less trouble,' she was wont to remark. 'Oh aye, that 'ud put the Betterware man in his place, that would.'

Auntie has carried on a lively flirtation with the Betterware man for years, but at my question, she shook her head. 'No, I ha'n't mentioned the helmet, not yet. I got to know him better afore I asks favours. Still, give me time. And now, my dear, that's gettin' late. Why not spend the night in my spare front 'stead o' takin' that long journey all on your lonesome? The bed's made up ready an' I'll have the kettle heatin' in a trice.'

I admit I was tempted, but it was no use. I'd ordered a new put-u-up and a double duvet, complete with cover (blue background, pink blossom; much more me than scarlet and black stripes) to replace the ones Matthew had taken, and they were being delivered next morning at 8.30 a.m. sharp. I had to be there to take them in.

I explained to Auntie that I couldn't stay on this occasion but would love to do so another time, and she toddled as far as the gate to wave me off. Outside it was pitch dark and moonless though behind the street lamps I could just make out the twinkling stars. The wind was strong though, and it was bitterly cold, so I got hastily into my beloved Astra, started the engine and drove off, waving to the small figure by the gate until it was out of sight. I knew she wouldn't go in until I and my car had disappeared, that was Auntie for you, so I didn't hang about. She feels the cold; old people do.

As soon as she was out of sight I settled down in my seat and concentrated; round the new roundabout, under the hospital bridge, up the hill and away! It was late and there seemed to be almost no traffic about, so I expected to make good time to Yarmouth.

It's a fair way, however, when you've no one to talk to, no one sitting in the passenger seat complaining about your driving. I didn't miss that, mind you; Matthew, who can't drive, is the world's most competent non-driver, or so he keeps telling me. I turned the radio on and sang along to Les Woodland's choice of music, which wasn't too bad, actually. But it meant I must have left Auntie's later than usual; even with picking up Matthew I was usually home by eleven. If I listened to Mr Woodland – and I often did – it was back at the flat, but now here I was, bowling along the dual carriageway with the cats' eyes winking at me and my voice competing with Phil Collins – sometimes drowning his lovely, creaky tones on the high notes – far from home, and bed, and Matthew.

Poor me! I felt sad for about ten seconds and then I remembered Matthew's cold feet on my warm bum, the smell of his socks when I'd managed to trick them off him for the wash and the hours he took on the loo whilst I yelled at him with crossed legs. It made his absence easier to bear, and when you add his infuriating habit of never telling me when he'd used the last of the toilet roll, and the way he would squeeze his zits too near the bathroom mirror so that the glass got splashed... well, I knew Auntie was right; I was better off alone. No more cold feet, smelly socks, unwanted advice, paperless sittings... the list just went on and on.

So I was in a lovely warm mood as I came up to the signpost for Acle, and perhaps that was why I turned off, because of course it's much quicker to stick to the main road. But Matthew and I often stopped in Acle for a bag of chips (and how he grumbled because I ate them whilst driving!), so in a way it was force of habit. As was the fact that I slowed down, in case the fuzz was lurking. Only at that time of night I needn't have worried; no one was about as I drove past the slumbering houses, just as dear Les said, sadly, that he was signing off and handing over to the World Service.

Heavens, it was midnight! I thought about switching to Radio One and Emma Freud but I wasn't in the mood; Steve Coe would be better, and anyway my car radio is tuned to Radio Norfolk so Broadland is just a twiddle away.

I got Steve, who was playing something smoochy from *Cats,* just as I swung out of Acle village (the chip shop was long shut or I might have treated myself to fifty pence worth) and on to the New Road.

And noticed, for the first time, how very dark it was and how incredibly lonely and endless the road ahead seemed.

It was daft, really. I knew the journey backwards and did it in darkness half the year, so I had become totally accustomed. My car was newish and well maintained – Matthew had his uses – so why should I suddenly feel so vulnerable? The road stretched ahead, straight as an arrow, gleaming black in the headlights' glare, the car purred along, the stars twinkled overhead – and I was afraid.

But of what? Of the *dark?* How ridiculous, of course I wasn't afraid of the dark! Of loneliness, then? Being alone in the car with no Matthew beside me? It couldn't be that, I've always rather enjoyed solitary driving.

The flat, then? Was I not enjoying the journey because I was going home to an empty flat? It is true that the approach to the flat, which is above a greengrocer's shop, is a bit scary. I have to unlock a large door, scoot up a flight of dark and narrow stairs and then unlock my own front door. Usually I tear up the stairs with my eyes shut, fumbling for my key as I run, and get it into the lock by osmosis, I believe. If I walk up the stairs and get my key out on the landing I take ages finding the keyhole. Eyes shut and at the double is best.

So I decided to do that tonight, because of that horrid story in the *Evening News*. I wouldn't hang around, I'd check that the street was empty and then charge as fast as I could for home and...

My thoughts broke off short. Ahead of me I could see something on the tarmac. Here, the road was just a dark ribbon laid out between the pollarded willows and beyond them, the flat water meadows, the grazing cattle, the occasional streak of a dyke, but there was definitely something on my half of the carriageway.

My sight is good but the road isn't as flat as it looks; I slowed, staring fixedly ahead. It was getting clearer; a hump, a lump, something long and thin, a garment flapping in the bitter wind – my God, it was a woman, lying where she had fallen in the road!

Like the coward that I am I slowed still further, straining to see what had happened ahead. Could she have fainted, or been knocked down by a hit-and-run driver? I dreaded blood, pain, something with which I should be unable to cope, but it never entered my head not to stop. I am no saint but I could no more pass by on the other side when someone is in trouble than – than you could!

I stopped four or five yards from the body and jumped out, suddenly anxious to reach her, to save, to succour. I ran the short distance between her and the car, the frozen grasses on the verge brushing my legs, my shadow leaping ahead of me, huge and frightening in the headlights. I fell on my knees beside her – and my heart gave a great, untidy thump of relief. It was not a woman, nor was it a man. It was a good-sized sack of something as yet unidentified, a huge

86

sugar beet with the shaggy top still on, and one of those blue fertiliser bags which abound in country areas.

As soon as my heart slowed to a more normal beat I stood up. Despite the cold my cheeks burned; what a fool I'd been! I turned back towards the car, angry with myself, then glanced over my shoulder. The sack woman was back, lying on my half of the carriageway. It was no flight of my overstretched imagination, it was an optical illusion which would have any passing motorist slamming on the brakes or taking evasive action which could easily end in an accident. It was, in short, a very real hazard.

I gave one wistful glance at my Astra, lights blazing, radio still playing, door invitingly ajar, then stomped back to the obstruction. I lifted the sack, not without difficulty for it was heavy, and slithered it into the ditch. Now that I had handled it I could tell it was full of spuds, knobbly and earth-smelling. Then I picked up the sugar beet and bowled it underarm on to the marsh for the cattle to enjoy.

As soon as I'd moved the sack the blue fertiliser bag had taken off of its own accord, flapping like a huge blue crow, temporarily suspended for a moment by the spiky, suppli-cating branches of a pollarded willow and then freeing itself with a desperate tug to disappear into the dark.

Satisfied that the sack woman would fool no one else, I walked back to the car and got behind the wheel. I was about to shut the door when I saw, in the driving mirror, another vehicle approaching fast, its lights jerking as it, too, negotiated the undulating road surface.

Damn, I thought. If there is one thing I hate it's driving with someone's headlights in my mirror, so I gunned the engine and got off to a racing start, the sack woman as good as forgotten.

But the driver behind me still came on, faster if anything, so I drew over to the verge. There was tons of room, no doubt he would dash past me and disappear in a flurry of red tail lights and trumpeting horn.

Only he didn't. He fell in behind me and began flashing his lights at me – it had to be at me, there wasn't another solitary soul about. What a time to play silly buggers, I thought; some men only have to see a girl driving a car and they try to chat her up, metaphorically if not actually. So I ignored him and continued to drive steadily, glancing at the clock as I did so. My God, it was nearly five and twenty to one – my stop had lost me more time than I'd realised. I glanced uneasily in my mirror. The other car had dropped back a bit but it was still too close for my liking and even as I looked he flashed his lights again; down, up; down, up.

Gently, with an even pressure of my foot on the accelerator, I speeded up. Equally gently, so did he. Smoothly, I braked a fraction, slowing to a moderate fifty. Equally smoothly, so did he.

It was not until then that it occurred to me what a fool I had been to stop on that lonely stretch of road. Just suppose the sack-woman had been, not an accidental grouping of objects, but a trick to get me to stop? The man in the car behind me might have meant to cut his lights and slide to a stop behind my car whilst I was investigating the 'body'. Then he could have crept up to me in the dark, as I knelt by the sack-woman, and put his clammy fingers round my throat...

The thought was so terrifying that my foot, of its own accord, began to squeeze the accelerator and I was doing eighty as I passed the Stracey Arms and the windmill in their brief sea of fluorescent light. Neither building showed so much as a candle's gleam and the windy darkness had swallowed me up again before I'd considered whether entering the street lights might discourage my pursuer. For pursuer he was now, a Beast with horns and a tail, out to terrify if not actually to devour, nipping at my heels one minute, drawing watchfully back the next, like a cat with a mouse. But always pursuing, never overtaking or falling right back, now flashing his lights, now gently pipping his horn, presumably in the hope that I'd think him a friend or acquaintance and stop.

But I knew no one who owned a white Ford Cosworth, thought almost everyone I know would love one. One glance in my mirror and I'd known it for the Cosworth RS500 from the very low spoiler, though I could not make out the fin on the back nor the elegant spoked wheels. And in a way the fact that I recognised the car made it worse; I knew it could outrun me, out-brake me, out-drive me. Yet I drove on, hands slippery on the wheel, crouching forward, attention divided between the road before and the pursuit behind. If only I'd not stopped to investigate the sack-woman I'd have been home long before the Cosworth came along. But at least I hadn't lingered long enough for him to catch up with me whilst I was crouching by the roadside. It was small comfort, but at least I'd been spared that, and I was still ahead and approaching Yarmouth and lights and civilisation as fast as I decently could.

Presently I slowed, to give him another chance to overtake, prove to be just a foolish young guy who had spotted a blonde ahead and wanted to impress her. But he slowed too as the marsh and its fringing willows flashed by, as a direction post – Great Yarmouth, 5 miles – did likewise. He began to raise and lower his lights again, this time more rapidly, almost as though he were signalling to me in Morse code. He was: three short flashes, three long, three short. SOS in any language. I'd been a Girl Guide for my sins and knew SOS and Mayday still, but I wasn't being tricked a second time. I gripped the wheel tighter and drove on, a little faster now. I couldn't outrun him, I knew that, but if I could get to Yarmouth, find people, perhaps a cop, then I would stop and confront my pursuer. If I couldn't, I'd – I'd have to think again.

I entered the outskirts of Yarmouth like a bat out of hell: the orange overhead lights illuminated the big roundabout and as I tore across, the hoardings and car pounds on the left – empty, of course. No help there. But I kept on going, a vague plan forming in the back of my mind. My pursuer was faster, possibly even a better driver, he certainly had the superior vehicle, but did he know Yarmouth as well as I did? As I zoomed into St Nicholas Street, with the church on my left and a quick glimpse of the market place on my right, I realised I was exceeding the speed limit by about thirty mph, but I didn't care a bit. If I was copped for speeding – oh joy!

I screeched past the red lights at the Nelson Road cross, a glance showing once more that there were to be no interested bystanders waving fists, calling the fuzz, just me, my sturdy Astra, the empty roads and my enemy.

I jigged to the left when the next junction came – I'd crossed another set of lights at red and one at green – and roared along Regent Road. Oh God, send me a copper who'll lock me up in a nice safe little cell, I prayed as the driver of the Cosworth began gently to toot his horn again. And when he began to toot SOS I cut another set of red lights, went round the huge floral roundabout on the prom and turned onto Marine Parade, passing Britannia Pier and various other edifices which separate the prom from the sea.

The Parade was deserted, wouldn't you know? Not a yob put a boot through the windscreen of a parked car – there were no parked cars – not a vandal sprayed paint over shrouded Joyland's jollities. The lights on the amusement arcades twinkled bravely enough, but no one saw them... no one but me and my enemy, that is. I must have slowed a fraction as I gazed hopefully about me and when I next glanced in my mirror, the Cosworth was almost on my bumper, giving rise to another fear; suppose he tried to ram me? That way he could be sure of my company!

Galvanised, I swung the car violently right, without giving it a moment's thought – and he went straight on. He did, he really did! But even as I roared down the side street which had opened up before me I saw his lights again as he did a tight U-turn and came after me.

But I had the start I'd been praying for and I didn't mean to lose it now. I cut my lights, took a left and then a right. I'm going to lose you, my friend, I told him. Reckless, regardless, never even thinking about help now, I twisted and turned through the myriad little streets behind the prom, no longer hurrying, deliberately slow, the engine purring on a low note which, I prayed, would prove difficult to hear even a street away.

I slowed to a very, very slow crawl. I inched along, nose almost pressed to the wheel, whilst the sweat dried on me and I began to think the nightmare was over. Here, there were plenty of parked cars though still no people, so I drove as close to them as I dared, and every now and then I wound down my window and listened. I heard an engine's note far away, fading, fading...

I must have lost him! Jubilant, I began to creep forward once more, suddenly realising that I was within a hundred yards of the flat. I could head for home now, because without my pursuer the flat seemed safety personified. Once inside it no one could hurt me, I could telephone the police, explain what had happened, demand protection...

My street is a quiet little cul-de-sac. I reached it. I knew just what to do, having belatedly remembered the murderer who was loose in Yarmouth, according to the *Evening News* and Auntie, anyway. He had strangled his victim whilst she sat in her car, outside her own home. So I would wait for a moment to make quite sure no one was lurking, and then make a run for it.

I drew quietly into a parking space almost directly in front of the greengrocer's shop and clicked the passenger lock, then peered all around me, and with my fingers actually around the door handle something made me check my mirror. And there it was, a dark moving shape, a car without lights. Smoothly as a striking snake he slid into the parking space behind me.

Suddenly I was no longer frightened, I was just angry. And I'd had enough. Damn him, I was within ten feet of my own front door, I would not be panicked into running again. I cut the engine and jumped out of the car and round it to the pavement, all in one movement. I saw his door open, saw him scramble out, but I was across the pavement like lightning, my key ready, both hands reaching for the door. He was a hefty chap, it would take him a second or two...

I never reached the door. He grabbed my arms and swung me round, he was saying something about stopping the car, did I know but I was past light conversation. I shrieked and

91

went to hit him, saw his mouth opening, a hand pointing back to my car and heard, for the first time, the voice of my enemy.

'Wait, love! Look at your car before you try to kill me – for the love of God, look at your car!'

It had to be a trick, yet so earnest, so compelling was the voice that I looked – and looked again.

The door I had just locked was slowly opening as if of its own volition. It swung wide and a figure, bent double, came scuttling out, long limbs bent like a spider. He was clad from head to foot in black but I caught a glimpse of a white, hollow-eyed face, the gape of an opening mouth fringed with horribly jagged teeth, and then he was running, still at a crouch, dodging down Dorset Close and out of sight.

I stopped pulling against my captor even as he let go of my arm and set off in pursuit. I felt sick and dizzy. Waves of nausea were washing over me, turning the stars in their places as though I was on the wildest fun-fair ride ever. I leaned against the car and then, suddenly, I saw the pavement getting closer and felt it hit my knees. I knew I was passing out, slowly and ingloriously, and there wasn't a darned thing I could do about it.

It could not have lasted for more than a minute or two; then someone spoke to me and a hand touched my shoulder. I knew it was the guy in the Cosworth.

'You all right, love? Come on, you've had a narrow escape but you're fine now... I'm back, I didn't catch him, but I got a bloody good look at him and it won't be long before that particular guy is behind bars, where he belongs. Come on, don't go fainting on me after you've led me such a chase. You're quite a driver, kid; if the fellers knew I'd been beaten by an Astra – and you just a slip of a thing – I'd never live it down!

You can say what you like, an admiring tone and a compliment or two can work wonders. We were right under a lamppost so I could see him clearly. Big, broad-shouldered, dark hair cut short, dark trousers, crisp white shirt with black epaulettes... my God, a cop! I'd been praying for a cop and all the time I was being chased by one!

'I – I jumped the lights,' I said weakly, remembering.

He nodded gravely. 'Once or twice.'

'I think I may have exceeded the speed limit a bit, too. I thought you were a murderer, you see. I'm awfully sorry.'

He smiled. 'You went the wrong way down one-way streets as well, but think nothing of it; I thought you were going to be a corpse, that's my problem. If I'd overtaken you and tried to pull you over you'd have roared straight past me and got away and – well, you'd probably have been the Spider's second victim in a week. What made you stop out on the marshes?

The sack-woman! It seemed so long ago, such a tiny incident, but it had started the whole horrible chain of events. I told him about it, trying not to let my voice shake.

'I see. And you didn't realise it was a put-up job? Whilst you were bending over your sack-woman Chummy was nipping into the back of your car. I saw his shadow in my headlights and tried to warn you, but you weren't having any. So he meant to lie low until you stopped, and then...'

His voice faded at my shudder, a shudder which shook my entire frame.

'Yes. So you see, love, you did have a narrow escape. I've no doubt he'd pulled the sack-woman trick before, which was how he caught his last victim. Most women will stop at an accident, no matter how dangerous it may be. Women are kind; impulsive, too. Whereas men tend to think fairly carefully before they act.'

'I'll think carefully in future,' I assured him in a small voice. 'You saved my life, didn't you? I'm tremendously grateful, really I am. I just don't know quite what to say.'

Then, like a fool, I gave the most enormous jaw-cracking yawn and started to bawl like an infant. I don't know what came over me, because I'm not the crying kind, I never shed a tear when Matthew walked out on me. My pursuer, or life-saver rather, put his arms round me and pulled me close so that I found myself weeping into his uniformed chest, and rather enjoying it. Well, he has got very strong, comforting arms.

'Look, you've had a horrid time,' he said when my sobs had begun to slacken. 'But I must get to a telephonc. Is there anyone at home here to take care of you?'

'No, no one,' I hiccuped. 'My b-boyfriend walked out on me ten days ago and I h'haven't found another flat-share yet. And I d-don't want to go up there in the dark all by myself.'

My rescuer stared down at me and I stared up at him, then he gave me a lovely, rueful grin. 'Perhaps you'd better come down to the station with me so I can keep an eye on you... only I know you ought to be tucked up in bed with a hot drink and some aspirin!'

I tugged myself free of his arms and shook my head. 'No. There are too many questions I want to ask. I'll come to the station with you. They'll want me as a witness later, anyway.'

And that was how I got my flat-share, in the end. And how Auntie got the longed-for policeman's helmet to hang inside her front door. It's a funny old world, isn't it? But if you're driving across Acle marshes one dark night and see what looks like a body on the road – think twice before you stop. You might not be as lucky as I was!

Just a Bit of Fun

Rosemary Walker

Rosemary Walker worked as a physiotherapist before taking early retirement in 1984. She graduated from the University of East Anglia with an Honours degree in Philosophy in 1991, and now devotes her time to writing and her garden. She has published articles on physiotherapy, a handbook for patients, *Coping with Arthritis*, and is currently working on a full-length crime story set in a physiotherapy department. She is married with three sons, and has lived in Suffolk since 1974.

The patient in intensive care stirred and muttered. Most of the head and face was so obscured by bandages that the young policewoman sitting beside the bed had difficulty in hearing. She leaned closer, but now the only sounds were the irregular ping of the machine, monitoring each heartbeat, and the soughing of the ventilator.

The young doctor finished his checks and made incomprehensible notes on the chart. He stood looking at his patient for a long moment, then smiled briefly at the waiting girl.

'A boring job, yours, I would have thought. How long have you been here?'

'Three days now. It's not all like this.' As he turned to go, she laid a hand on his sleeve.

'What are the chances? Is it possible to survive those injuries?'

'Who knows?' he said. 'People have survived worse damage than that, but I wouldn't take a bet on it. We can only wait and see.'

I forced my eyelids open as I struggled up from beneath the suffocating weight of guilt and fear. In the first dawn light I looked at my watch. Five-thirty. I'd had the dream again. I lay there desolate, horrified. Could I really have killed at some time in my past and have no knowledge of it now except deep in my subconscious? Could I have murdered another human being without it leaving a trace in my memory? Only in this ever-recurring dream smothering me in a black choking blanket of panic, from which I awoke sweating and terrified.

I didn't dream it every night, of course. If I had, I think I would have gone mad by now. Sometimes it stayed away for months. While I had been at university working hard for Finals, I hadn't dreamed it for a year. I thought it had gone away for ever, but now a week did not pass by without it recurring.

If only I could remember more, perhaps I would feel better. If I knew who might have died, and where, perhaps I could exorcise this horror. All I knew was that someone was dead – I thought it was a woman, but I couldn't be sure. Two things were constant: there was blood, blood everywhere, and I was deeply involved.

Mingled with the relief of waking was the aftertaste, oppressive and chilling. Each time I woke, I was more frightened.

I didn't want to go back to sleep, so I got up and made a pot of tea. I took it back to bed, and turned on the radio for the early morning news. It was as depressing as ever. Bosnia, the European Union, the government, Rwanda. You could have listened to the news any time during the last couple of years and it would have been the same. But at least I wasn't responsible for the slaughter in Bosnia, the genocide in Rwanda. I drank my tea, and lit a cigarette. Smoking in bed was one of the pleasures restored by living alone again. How Patrick had hated it.

I lay there thinking. In the cold light of day my terrors receded. It was only a dream – insane to think it had any basis in reality. But if not, why did it keep returning? I tried to think rationally. Perhaps I should accept that deep down there was something I had done which my conscious mind rejected. Assume, therefore, that someone had indeed died as a result of my actions. An accident, perhaps? No, this killing, if killing there had been, was accompanied by hate, and jealousy, and intent. Whatever else was blurred in the dream, that much was clear. So where did I go next?

Two questions. First, who was there in my past whom I had hated enough to kill, with that degree of loathing and satisfaction at the crunch of metal on bone? I sat up suddenly. At last I had become aware of method, that the murder weapon was metal. If I progressed in this logical fashion, maybe more would emerge. Part of me really didn't want to know, but my rational self said anything was better than this.

Second, when? Well, Patrick had certainly gone. My marriage had lasted five years, to everyone's surprise, including mine. I hadn't hated him enough to kill him, though. We just drifted apart. The day I came home to find that he had gone, bags packed, classic note upon the mantelpiece, I was relieved more than anything. A nice enough guy, but not for me – not after five years anyway. It was difficult now to remember the sexual passion which had characterised the early days of our marriage. When I first met Patrick it really had been a case of 'seeing a stranger across a crowded room'.

The French call it 'coup de foudre'. But when the passion cooled there was nothing left. Not a good basis for a marriage. For God's sake, what had I been thinking of? The truth was, thinking hadn't much to do with it. It had been my hormones screaming yes, yes, yes.

Who else was there? My parents were dead, but they had died of the things parents die of – cancer, a heart attack – so I didn't think I could have killed either of them. Anyway I'd rather liked them. Not very bright, but well-meaning, and Sandra's mother was still alive when I last heard, a long-stay patient at St Andrews.

My parents had been bewildered when my teachers had suggested I should go to university.

'What's wrong with a job?' my mum had said. 'You're a clever girl, you could get a good job with good prospects.' The implication was that I should be like Sandra. My father had been married before, and Sandra was my half-sister. When we were young she had mothered me, although I had a perfectly good mother of my own. She had always been maternal, domestic, tailor-made for marriage and children.

Sandra had a job as a cashier in Jarrolds, a big step up from working in a factory, but not for me. They hadn't understood then that I was different, special.

I suppose we'd been close in our younger days. I had always been her baby sister, to be loved and pampered and fussed over, before I outgrew her. I realised quite early on that I was cleverer than she, but it took her a lot longer, and even then she tried to pretend it wasn't so. Sandra would never have made it to university. A levels were beyond her – just a clutch of O's in things like typing and home economics. She had been dismayed to find her baby sister outstripping her.

Poor old Sandy, a cashier's job for a year or two, followed by marriage and kids, was the height of her ambition. Even I had to admit she was very pretty, and she was a sensational cook. Why she didn't take up cooking as a career when she left school was beyond me, but Jarrolds offered security and good pay. Jarrolds was an old-established and respected store in the centre of Norwich, and working there was a role my family understood. Cooking for a living smacked too much of being a servant. Sandra's mother had been in service, and that was something she wasn't going to do.

I tried to persuade her that it needn't be like that – she could set up for herself, form a business, but that concept was beyond her, and beyond my parents as well.

'What does she want to do something like that for?' Dad had asked. 'She'll give up work when she gets married.' They beamed fondly at her. 'Don't expect that'll be long, eh?'

Given all this I wasn't surprised when she got engaged to a chap who worked with Dad on the rigs. I was away at university at the time, working for my Ph.D., and the deadline for my thesis was getting perilously close, so I didn't get home until the day of the engagement party.

Once they had accepted the idea of university, Mum and Dad had expected me to go to the University of East Anglia. It had a good reputation in geological sciences, and would be most people's choice, but UEA was in Norwich, and that would have meant living at home, so I settled for Southampton instead.

The party was well under way when I arrived. I pushed through the crowd which seemed to consist largely of enormous young men and their girlfriends swigging down lager as fast as they could go. I remembered that Dad had said Sandra's intended was a keen footballer, and it looked as if the whole team, complete with reserves, was here tonight. The air was thick with cigarette smoke, and swelteringly hot.

Sandra was at a side table, dishing out the drinks, her face flushed and sweating.

'Hi Sandy,' I said. 'Sorry I'm late.'

'Oh, you've made it, have you? I was beginning to think you'd decided all this was beneath you.' I stared at her. What was that little barb for, I wondered?

'Where's the boyfriend?' I asked. 'I'm dying to meet him.'

'Over there somewhere.' She jerked her head in the direction of the scrum. 'Someone will introduce you. And when you find him, tell him I could do with a hand over here.' She turned back to the bar.

'Leave it, Sandra,' I urged. 'They'll help themselves.'

'I'm sure they will, which is the reason I can't leave it.'

'I'll do it,' I said. 'I don't know anyone here to talk to. It's your party, go and enjoy it.'

She gave me what Mum would have called an old-fashioned look. 'They don't want to talk to me, they can talk to me any time. They'd much rather talk to my brilliant young sister.' She slammed a can of lager into the hands of a thirsty guest.

This wasn't like Sandy. She was never spiteful. Rages, yes, furious outbursts of temper which flared and died as quickly as they had come. She must have seen my surprise.

'If you must know, I can't wait to get married and away from here. Mum and Dad never stop boasting about you. I'm sick to death of the sound of your name.'

I decided to sort all this out later. I took a drink and pushed my way across the room. My eye was caught by a tall, good-looking young man surrounded by a noisy crowd. How fit they all looked. Physically at least, they were a great improvement on the pale and acne'd students I'd been mixing with lately. Pretty thick though, probably. The tall young man was very brown, and looked as if he spent a good deal of time out of doors. At that moment he turned his head, and we looked at each other. As I said, 'coup de foudre' – instant sexual recognition.

We left the noisy smoky party together, and went to a

nearby pub. It was much later that I discovered Patrick was my sister's betrothed, but by that time it was too late for both of us. Too late for Sandra too, I'm afraid.

I went back to university next morning without seeing her again. My parents made it clear over breakfast that they thought I had behaved badly, but I didn't care. I struggled through the final weeks of term, obsessed by Patrick. Fortunately I had almost finished my thesis, or I would never have got my doctorate. He came up whenever his job would let him. Looking back, I can see now how awkward and gauche my friends must have found him, but I was so infatuated I didn't notice.

As soon as term was over, Patrick and I were married. Only my mother came to the wedding. Neither my father nor Sandra had spoken to me since the engagement party. My father wrote saying how badly Sandra had taken it, and how appallingly I was behaving. I chucked the letter away. Patrick and I wanted each other, and that was all there was to it. Even if I gave him up, which I had no intention of doing, he wouldn't have gone back to her.

It took about a year for it to become obvious to both of us that we had absolutely nothing in common except sex. I had been astounded to find that Patrick had expected me to stay at home once we were married, and plunge into childbearing. 'Why,' he had asked plaintively, 'did we get married, if not to have kids?' I explained as kindly as I could that I had far too good a brain to waste my most creative years wiping noses and bottoms, and waiting at school gates. I had reluctantly offered to have a child, on the clear understanding that he would give up work to look after it. His reaction was entirely predictable. What would his mates think? Worse, what would they say behind his back?

There wasn't much of the marriage left after a couple of years, but we soldiered on. I wasn't often at home. Things were coming to a head with my research, and I was doing a lot of travelling at this time, reading papers at conferences, getting myself known. I don't know what Patrick did with his time when he wasn't on the rig. He did shifts of ten days on, ten days off, so even when I was at home we rarely coincided.

The weekend after my paper was published I went home. It was the first time for weeks and as I said, he'd gone. Oh, the blessed peace of the empty flat. It was as if he'd never been there. I spent the weekend sleeping and pottering. I had no idea where he'd gone, and really didn't care. I supposed he had gone back to live with his parents.

The fear and depression left by the dream had passed. I could think about Patrick without a qualm. If I had killed anyone, it wasn't him. I wondered about my colleagues. The academic world is full of jealousy and political in-fighting. Had I felt enough ill will towards any of my colleagues to take such drastic measures? I had made enemies, of course. My field was too small, too incestuous, for me not to have made enemies. Anyone who is successful will, but nothing about my work triggered any emotion, and anyway, I'd been having the dream long before I started work.

I felt so much better that by the time I had showered I had forgotten about it, but that night it came back, worse than ever. The blood, anger and violence were there in full measure, but once again the identity of the victim was hidden from me.

Who was it?

There was nothing for it, I thought, as I lay shaking and terrified in the dark. I would have to get in touch with Sandra.

I put off trying to contact her for a week or two. For one thing, I was very busy, and for another I was nervous about stirring anything up. Suppose my enquiries made her suspicious? It would sound odd to say the least, if I said, 'Is there anyone we knew who isn't around any more?' Sandra had no reason to be well disposed towards me. Might I not be putting in hand a train of enquiry which could result in my arrest and imprisonment?

I decided in the end to ask her if she had any photos of Mum and Dad I could have. It was true that I hadn't got any. Sandra had inherited the house and all its contents when they died. My mother was an inveterate photographer, and I remembered fat albums bursting with snaps of our friends and relations. Perhaps I might have a look at those. As a story it was a bit thin – I'd never been in the least interested in family photos before – but even if there was anything doubtful in my past, I didn't think it would arouse her suspicion. Sandra always had to have things spelled out for her before she grasped their implications.

My sister still lived in my parents' old house in Norwich. As I walked along the familiar street I realised it must be nearly ten years since I had been here. Not since the engagement party, in fact. Dad had bought the little late-Victorian terraced house long before the area became known as 'The Golden Triangle'. With the building of the university on the outskirts of Norwich in the sixties, it had become extremely popular. Within walking distance of both campus and city centre, property there was very much in demand. The streets were a mixture of houses in need of paint, with unkempt gardens, as owners let to students at minimum outlay to themselves, and the trim and glossy homes of house-proud first-time buyers.

My home street had come up in the world. Money had been spent, not always wisely, on renovation and modernisation. The pretty sash windows in many places had vanished in favour of unsuitable double glazing, and some of the front gardens had become free standing for cars. The destruction of the gardens was a pity, but I could understand the reason for it. Parking in those narrow streets must be a nightmare.

I started counting the houses. 45, 43, 41 – the one I wanted was 39. I stood aghast. Oh Sandra, I thought, not stone cladding! How could she do it? But in a way I wasn't surprised. She had always been a Crimplene and flowered pinafore girl. Why not stone cladding?

She answered the door at my second ring. She looked different, and for a moment I wondered what it was. Then I realised she was pregnant, and her face had that bovine, smoothed-out look that some women get in pregnancy. The 'everything for the best, in the best of all possible worlds' look. Someone had told me she'd got married a year or two back, but I had forgotten.

She looked at me for a long time before she opened the door wider. 'You'd better come in.'

'Nice to see you again, Sandy.' I was determinedly cheerful. She didn't answer. I stepped into the tiny hall. The front door had originally led straight into the front room, but a glazed cubicle had been erected around the door, keeping out the draughts. It was all very neat and spotless. I tried again.

'You're looking well,' I said.

'I've looked out those photographs you asked for.' She gestured to a pile of albums on the highly polished table. 'You can take them away with you, as long as you bring them back.'

'If there are any I want, I'll get them copied,' I agreed.

As a social event the visit wasn't a success, but then I hadn't come to establish cosy relations. Just to chat about friends we used to have in common, which might give me a lead. I suppose it was with this in mind that I said as I was leaving, my arms full of albums, 'Have you seen anything of Patrick since we split up?'

I could have kicked myself the moment it was out. It wasn't the most tactful remark, if I wanted to get on any sort of terms with Sandra. She gave me a look which was pure hostility, and shut the door in my face.

It was some weeks before I went there again. I'd been through all the albums carefully, but no face had emerged that seemed even remotely promising. There were lots of people I'd totally forgotten, but they were those with whom I'd had the slightest of contacts, people briefly known and discarded. No one to be a cause of such anger and pain.

There were several snaps of me and Sandra with Mum and Dad when we were little, which filled me briefly with a sort of nostalgia. Two small girls in flowered dresses and white ankle socks, with hair tied in bunches. I thought I'd have one or two of them copied, if only to give credence to my story.

I packed them all into the back of my car ready for returning. Sandra had asked me to ring before I went again, but one afternoon I unexpectedly found myself in the area, and decided to drop in on the off-chance. If I saw a phone box I'd call, but the only one I found had been vandalised.

There was a man in the garden of the stone-clad house, weeding, or staking out, or whatever it is you do to plants. His back was towards me, but as I approached he straightened up and turned.

We stared at each other.

'Patrick,' I said unbelievingly, and then again, 'Patrick?'

He was as handsome as ever, still as fit and tanned. He still looked as if he spent a lot of time in the open air. I was back ten years and felt the familiar shiverings of desire.

'What are you doing here?' I said.

'I could ask the same of you.' He wiped his earthy hands on his jeans. 'I live here.'

'You live here?' My tone was incredulous.

'Didn't you know that Sandy and I were married?'

'Married? To Sandra? You can't be, you're married to me.'

'We were divorced, remember? Sandy and I have been married nearly two years now.'

I wanted to hit him. A curious mixture of emotions filled me. Anger, jealousy, and when I thought of the pregnancy, a sort of revulsion. How could he do this to me? He had been mine, how could he have gone back to her? I tried to remind myself of the reasons I hadn't wanted him any more, but I still couldn't bear the thought of my sister having him. I felt sick.

I managed to say, 'Is Sandra in?' in what I hoped was a normal voice.

'She visits her mother on Tuesdays,' he said. 'She won't be back for a couple of hours yet. I was just about to make myself some tea. Would you like some?'

We drank it at the kitchen table. The back garden, seen through the window, was full of vegetables. I gestured towards it. 'Is that your work?'

'It is. I really like gardening. We're pretty nearly self-sufficient for veg. I'm thinking of putting in an asparagus bed next spring.'

'A bit up-market for Sandy, I would have thought?'

Somehow the thought of all this cosy domesticity increased my anger and jealousy. I didn't want it for myself, no way, I'd be bored to tears again in no time, but somehow I felt deprived of something valuable. I stood up abruptly.

'I must go,' I said. 'I only came to deliver some photos. They're in the car.'

'I'll come and get them,' said Patrick. 'Where are you living, now you're rich and successful?'

'You have an odd idea of the salaries paid to researchers if you think I'm rich. I'm still living in the old flat.'

God, he smelled marvellous, that wonderful masculine smell of healthy flesh, fresh sweat, the loamy moist smell of earth still clinging to him. It was ages since I'd been to bed with anyone. I wanted to touch him, to run my fingers along that tanned forearm.

Trying to speak lightly, I said, 'Call in and see it sometime. I've made a few changes.' I got in the car, with an effort added, 'Bring Sandy,' and drove away.

It was a Tuesday again when he called. I thought it might be. Sandra's day to visit her mother.

'Don't you have to work?' I asked.

'Ten days on, ten days off, remember?'

His ostensible reason for coming was to bring me more photos. He held out a large manila envelope.

'I brought you these. They weren't with the others, I'd hidden them away.'

When I took them out, I could see why. They were mostly of our wedding, Patrick and me, Mum and a couple of his mates outside the Register Office, but a few were taken on holiday a few weeks later. I remembered one particularly. We'd been out all day on the beach, swimming, walking and scrabbling about in rock pools as if we were ten years old. In the photo, we were sitting outside a small pub where we'd stopped to eat before driving home. A couple at the next table had snapped us with their camera. It had been a hot day, just beginning to cool towards evening. The photograph brought back vividly that slightly sandy, gritty feeling of a day spent on the beach, skin tightening with the beginnings of sunburn, calves aching with unaccustomed exercise. We had our arms around each other. I looked up from the photographs. He was watching me intently.

'Oh Patrick,' I said, and suddenly we were in each other's arms.

We saw each other fairly regularly after that. Our meetings weren't that frequent because of his shifts, and Sandra visited her mother only once a week. It seemed to me a very satisfactory arrangement. In fact, I thought, if I had seen Patrick this infrequently before we might have managed to stay married.

We spent our afternoons together in bed. Sex had never been one of our problems. It was as good as ever, and fortunately it didn't leave much time for conversation. It suited me fine, but as Sandra became more absorbed in ante-natal classes and clinical checks, all involving regular absences from home, Patrick became more demanding.

'After it's born,' he said, 'she won't be going to ante-natal classes any more, or visit her mother so much.'

'She'll be going to the baby clinic,' I said reassuringly.

'Not so often.'

I can't say I was too upset at the prospect. The familiar pricklings of boredom were occasionally making themselves felt. I was getting slightly uneasy about the way Patrick's thoughts were going.

'We can't go on like this,' he said once or twice, and then one day, 'I think we ought to tell her.'

To gain time I said, 'Tell her what?' but I didn't have to ask. He wanted to get a divorce, for us to get back together, get married again. Damn Patrick, why did he have to be so conventional, always wanting marriage and respectability?

I hedged about a definite reply. I wasn't ready yet to give up the affair entirely.

'What about the baby? You wanted kids. You can't just

push off and leave her to cope alone.' He admitted there was a problem. 'And Sandy adores you,' I said.

After this the dreams started getting worse again. Two or three times a week I'd wake in the small hours, sweating and shaking. It became more real, and several times I began to think that the face I sought was about to be revealed to me.

As the date of the birth grew nearer, Patrick became more pressing. 'Come on,' he kept saying. 'We'll have to tell her sometime. Why not now?'

Not even to have someone there when I awoke after one of the dreams, would I take on Patrick permanently again. I persuaded him it would be kinder to leave things as they were until after the baby was born. I should have made a clean break then, but to be honest, I was beginning to be a bit afraid of what he might do. In desperation I started looking at job vacancies abroad. Any ideas I had harboured of retaining him as a discreet entertainment for a rainy afternoon had gone.

One evening I was in the flat when the doorbell rang. It couldn't be Patrick, he was on the rig, and I didn't encourage casual droppers-in.

Sandra stood at the door. She was huge; the baby had to be due any day. Her face was bloated and her eyes full of misery. Sandra's world was no longer the best of all possible worlds.

'He told me,' she said flatly.

Oh Patrick, you fool, I thought. What a time to choose. I turned and walked into the living room.

'What has he told you?'

'You two want to get married again. He told me he doesn't love me, he's never loved me like he loved you.'

Of course not, I thought, what did she expect? But I had more sense than to say so, unlike stupid Patrick. I decided I must do what I should have done weeks before, and put a stop to this.

'It's not true,' I said. 'I don't love him, and I don't want him back. He's kidding himself.'

She looked bewildered. 'But why? He says you – you've

been seeing each other for months. What do you mean...?'

'Oh Sandra,' I said impatiently. 'It was only a bit of fun, a bit on the side, if you like.'

Her voice rose. 'A bit of fun? You've ruined my life for a second time for a bit of fun? I don't believe you, you're just pretending.'

She looked desperate. Her hair was clinging to her head in damp strands. I was terrified she might to into labour at any minute. How long did babies take? I had to get it into her head that it was over.

'I've finished with him, Sandra. He's beginning to bore me.'

As soon as the words were out I knew I'd made a mistake. One of her sudden rages engulfed her.

'He's boring?' she screamed. 'You've taken him from me again, and now that's it, you're bored?' She looked around.

'Sandra!' I said, and took a step towards her. She snatched up a brass candlestick from the mantelpiece and swung it wildly. Her huge bulk took her off balance, and she missed me by inches. 'Be careful,' I yelled. 'Don't be stupid, you could kill me.'

'I mean to,' she said, through stiff lips. 'I want to, I hate you.'

She swung the candlestick down on the side of my head, and I heard the crunch of metal on bone as my skull exploded.

Before the blackness engulfed me, I at last saw the face from my dream. It was my own.

Seventeenth-Century Justice

The Trial of the Lowestoft Witches

Robert Church

Robert Church served for twenty-six years in the Metropolitan Police, followed by ten years as a probation officer before taking early retirement. He now writes full time. He has had three non-fiction crime books published, and contributes articles regularly to *The Criminologist*. He is a member of the Crime Writers' Association, the Society of Authors and the British Society of Criminology. He lives with his wife in Lowestoft.

The two elderly widows standing in the dock at Bury St Edmunds on 10 March 1662[*] were victims of mid-seventeenth century superstition. Accused of witchcraft, their poverty, illiteracy and deformity (one was lame and the other hunch-backed) did little to endear them to their neighbours.

Amy Denny and Rose Cullender were indicted with 'bewitching Elizabeth and Ann Durent; Jane Bocking; Susan Chandler: William Durent; Elizabeth and Deborah Pacy.' Both women pleaded not guilty.

Their appearance in the dock before Sir Matthew Hale, Lord Chief Baron of His Majesty's Court of Exchequer, and Mr Justice Kelyng of the King's Bench Division, had resulted from a series of incidents involving their neighbours' children in Lowestoft.

The trial engendered considerable interest with lawyers, doctors and landowners in court, while outside a crowd of townsfolk quickly spread word of the proceedings around Bury and the surrounding countryside. The dramatic and sometimes bizarre evidence, although fulfilling the citizenry's expectations, was listened to with scepticism by several of the more discerning observers in court.

The name of the prosecuting barrister was not disclosed in either contemporary reports or subsequent accounts of the trial while, as was usual, the accused women were unrepresented. This omission was justified on the grounds that the burden of proof required to secure a conviction was so great as to render any defence argument futile. Defendants, many of whom were illiterate, inarticulate or both, were nevertheless entitled to cross-examine witnesses.

The prosecution opened the case against Amy Denny and Rose Cullender by telling of how during November 1659 Edmund Durent, a fisherman and father of three children,

---

[*] Some sources give the year of the trial as 1664 or 1665. My research indicates 1662 as the most likely date.

had refused to sell some fish to Cullender, much to her resentment. Soon afterwards a strange episode occurred involving Durent's wife Dorothy and Amy Denny over a baby-sitting arrangement.

It was Dorothy who first hobbled into court on crutches to tell of the event. She testified of leaving her youngest child William in the care of the elderly woman (despite knowing her reputation as a witch), with strict instructions that she was not to attempt to suckle the infant should it become hungry. Despite the injunction, Amy Denny endeavoured to feed the fractious baby, but succeeded only in inducing wind. Later she unwisely informed the child's mother of what she had done.

Dorothy Durent was predictably annoyed at this disobedience to her instructions, and became even more incensed that night when 'The child fell into strong fits...'

William's indisposition continued for several weeks until finally his mother took him to see Doctor Jacob at Great Yarmouth, a pseudo-medical practitioner with a reputation for helping bewitched children. Jacob's suggested remedy was odd: to 'Wrap up the child's blanket in the chimney corner all day; put the child to bed in it at night, and if you find anything else in it, throw it into the fire.'

The witness described how that evening, as she prepared to wrap William in the blanket, a toad had emerged from its folds and jumped along the hearth. She had managed to grab the hapless amphibian with a pair of tongs which she had then thrust into the fire. '...it made a great and horrible noise,' she said. '...after a space there was a flashing in the fire like gunpowder, making the noise like the discharge of a pistol, and thereupon the toad was no longer seen nor heard.'

As those in court digested the repugnant details of the toad's demise, Mrs Durent continued. Pointing to Amy Denny she stated that the next morning she had visited the old woman at home where she had found her to be suffering from burns to her face, legs and thighs, sustained, Dorothy maintained, at the time the toad had been consigned to the flames. All eyes turned to look at Amy Denny in the dock, but any scars remaining were concealed beneath her voluminous skirt and the grime on her face.

The witness went on to say that in the following March, 1660, Amy Denny visited her ten-year-old daughter Elizabeth and 'afflicted' her by giving her a glass of water. This inoffensive act had incensed Dorothy who had remonstrated with the accused. Denny had replied by invoking death upon Elizabeth, and lameness upon her mother. Strangely, the girl died three days later, and soon afterwards Dorothy came to rely upon crutches.

The trial so far had consisted solely of verbal testimony. Hereafter the proceedings were to be enlivened by the appearance in court of Denny and Cullender's alleged victims, coupled with demonstrations of the two women's occult power.

Samuel Pacy, father of eleven-year-old Elizabeth and her sister Deborah who was nine, was another fisherman who had incurred the displeasure of Amy Denny by refusing to sell her any herrings; Denny had departed muttering imprecations. According to Pacy, Deborah had soon afterwards experienced violent, painful fits, so much so that she was still too ill to attend the trial. Elizabeth, who had suffered similarly and was apparently unconscious, was nevertheless carried into the courtroom where later she was to participate in a dramatic demonstration.

The girls' father told the court that Deborah's malady had persisted throughout the previous October, during which period she had hallucinated, seeing Denny and calling out her name. Eventually he had summoned a Doctor Feaver, but he failed to diagnose or cure the problem. In view of this, and of Amy Denny's reputation as a witch, Pacy had had the old woman set in the stocks.

Two days later, on 30 October 1661, his elder daughter Elizabeth began having fits. She was unable to open her mouth and had to be forcibly fed, an indignity soon to be inflicted upon Deborah. Both girls continued to experience hallucinations, seemingly terrified by visions of both Amy Denny and Rose Cullender. Samuel Pacy added that besides also suffering lameness, deafness and temporary blindness, both daughters were painfully averse to being touched.

At this point Judge Hale intervened. He instructed Amy Denny to leave the dock and to touch the hand of Elizabeth Pacy who lay recumbent upon a wooden pallet in the well of the court. As Amy complied, Elizabeth jerked upright, grabbed hold of the woman's hand and then scratched her face. She accompanied this display by screaming at the top of her voice. While this impressed some observers, several distinguished lawyers in court, including Mr Serjeant Keeling, Mr Serjeant Earl and Mr Serjeant Barnard, were more sceptical. These doubts were shared by Lord Cornwallis of Eye and the premier Baronet of England, Sir Edmund Bacon of Redgrave, who were also present.

Encouraged by the response of his peers, Samuel Pacy went on to describe how he had subsequently witnessed Elizabeth and Deborah regurgitating a large quantity of pins and other ironmongery. To back up this astonishing revelation he produced a number of steel pins and broad-headed nails.

In a further effort to combat these continuing afflictions Pacy had tried exorcism, enjoining his daughters to read the New Testament. This again proved ineffective, the fits continuing with the girls reeling and spinning around the room while simultaneously hallucinating.

Finally, in the hope that a change of air might effect a

cure, Pacy had sent Elizabeth and Deborah to stay with his sister Margaret Arnold in Great Yarmouth. Mrs Arnold at first had been dubious about her nieces' alleged sufferings, but she became more sympathetic after seeing their digestive systems continue to expel pins and other metal objects. However, when they chased imaginary mice and poultry around her house before pretending to throw them onto the fire, her doubt and bewilderment returned.

Edward Durent, Dorothy's husband, described how earlier after he had refused to sell herrings to Rose Cullender, his other daughter Ann had suffered stomach pains and swooning attacks, in addition to vomiting pins and seeing visions of Cullender. Although present in court Ann was unable to testify, not having recovered from a fit she had fallen into immediately upon sighting Cullender in the dock.

Similar testimony was given in respect of Jane Bocking and Susan Chandler, both named in the indictment. Their mothers Mrs Diana Bocking and Mrs Mary Chandler each recalled her daughter hallucinating and seeing visions of the accused women, and stated that the girls had similarly been struck dumb periodically and had vomited up metal pins.

Eighteen-year-old Susan Chandler, the oldest victim, was present in court, but after becoming mute and suffering a fit she had to be taken from the room. Later she recovered sufficiently to return and take the oath, but immediately she was questioned she had another fit, her only contribution to the proceedings thereafter being a shrieked demand to 'Burn her, burn her.' This, in effect, ended the testimony of the victims and their relatives.

The dour, humourless Doctor Thomas Browne of Norwich was potentially the most influential witness at the trial of the Lowestoft witches. While it was suspected that Doctor Jacob of Great Yarmouth was in fact a tailor masquerading as a medical practitioner, no such doubt surrounded Browne whose eminence in the field of medicine was to be recognised by a knighthood in 1671. The author of *Religio Medici* and other learned tracts, Browne was acknowledged as 'a person of great knowledge'. It followed that his testimony considerably influenced the jury.

Doctor Browne informed the court that in Denmark recently witches had been unmasked who stuck pins, needles and nails into their victims; he went on to say that in his opinion the symptoms and manifestations that had reportedly afflicted the victims of the Lowestoft witches were consistent with the latter having consorted with the devil.

Despite Browne's testimony, the accused women were not entirely without allies in court. Three of them, Lord Cornwallis, Sir Edmund Bacon and Mr Serjeant Keeling, openly expressed their doubt at the evidence, much to the irritation of Sir Matthew Hale.

To counter their doubts and criticisms, the judge instigated a farcical course of action that was to cause a courtroom furore. Susan Chandler, who was in the middle of another fit, was manoeuvred to the side of the court where she was joined by Amy Denny, Chandler was then blindfolded before a female spectator was ushered forward and instructed to touch the girl. At the touch Chandler abruptly emerged from her fit, provoking some mirth among the spectators which was quickly silenced by the irate judge. To add to Sir Matthew Hale's discomfiture, Cornwallis, Bacon and Keeling were quick to point out that in view of Susan Chandler's reaction 'they did believe the whole transaction of this business was a mere imposture.'

Unquestionably the exercise had cast doubt on the veracity of the case against Denny and Cullender. Samuel Pacy made the issue even more confusing by suggesting that Susan Chandler had been deceived into believing a witch had touched her. He added ambiguously that while deprived of her understanding during the fit, she could nevertheless have been able to comprehend what was taking place.

Unfortunately for the accused women, the criticism and doubts raised by Lord Cornwallis, Sir Edmund Bacon and Mr Serjeant Keeling as a result of the demonstration were premature. Had they refrained from making their observations until the prosecution had demonstrably ended its case, the impact would have been greater, and fresh in the jury's minds when they retired. Instead their intervention gave the prosecution barrister the opportunity to introduce three more witnesses to bolster his case.

John Soam, a yeoman from Lowestoft, recalled that when passing Rose Cullender's cottage while riding on his cart, he had accidentally damaged a window. Rose not surprisingly had been annoyed. When subsequently the same cart had twice overturned, Soam had attributed these mishaps to Cullender's malign influence, rather than to any defect in the vehicle.

Two years previously an even more capricious series of events appeared to have overtaken farmer Robert Sheringham. Sheringham recounted how the axle of his wagon had inadvertently damaged the wall of Cullender's house. This had provoked her into making threats of dire consequences that would befall the farmer and his horses. Subsequently four of his horses and an unspecified number of cattle died; Sheringham had considered himself fortunate merely to have been struck lame. In a final imaginative sally, Sheringham explained that simultaneously he had become infested with lice, necessitating the burning of two of his coats.

The final witness was Ann Sandeswell, the wife of Amy Denny's landlord. She said that Denny had complained that the chimney of her house was in danger of collapsing if it was not repaired, a grievance disputed by the Sandeswells. However, when Denny's apprehension was vindicated by the collapse of the chimney, the landlord and his wife attributed it to their tenant's power of witchcraft. Ann Sandeswell added whimsically that Amy Denny had also bewitched her flock of geese.

The testimony of these three witnesses with their tales of equine death, lice infestation, toppling chimneys and bewitched geese, however unlikely it may have seemed, clouded over memory of the earlier, convincing demonstration.

Before Sir Matthew Hale started his summing-up, Amy Denny and Rose Cullender were invited to speak in their own defence. Objects of curiosity to everyone packed into the court room, besides being overawed by their surroundings, it is hardly surprising that they declined the offer.

Sir Matthew's summing-up was brief. He told the jury that there were only two matters for them to consider: one, whether or not the children had been bewitched, and two, whether the prisoners at the bar were guilty of that bewitching.

Hale made no mention either of the absurdities that had characterised much of the prosecution evidence or of the reliability of the witnesses. He also totally ignored the Susan Chandler demonstration. He said that he had no doubt that witches existed, the scriptures so confirming, and added that all nations had laws against witchcraft, endorsing their belief in the existence of witches.

Hale's pronouncements were rarely challenged. It was said that his method of arguing with counsel and giving judgement was 'severe and refined'. It can certainly be said that at the trial of the Lowestoft witches his judgement was severe, albeit lacking in refinement.

Hale instructed the jury to 'observe the evidence'; and to call for God's guidance in so doing, 'For to condemn the innocent and to let the guilty go free were both an abomination to the Lord.'

The jury retired for only half an hour before re-entering

court to announce that they had found Amy Denny and Rose Cullender guilty on all the indictments. Neither woman was sentenced immediately; instead they were taken back to gaol to await judgement on the morrow.

The following morning before the court reconvened, an extraordinary and irregular meeting took place. Elizabeth and Deborah Pacy with their father, Ann Durent and her parents, and Susan Chandler accompanied by her mother, stood before Sir Matthew Hale at his lodgings. The Pacy sisters and Ann Durent appeared to have recovered completely from their afflictions, but Susan Chandler was still subdued. Hale was delighted to hear from their parents that the restoration to health of their offspring, and the resultant transformation in their image, had occurred within half an hour of Denny and Cullender being convicted. For Sir Matthew Hale it was confirmation of his own convictions.

Later that same morning as Sir Matthew prepared to sentence the convicted women, Elizabeth and Deborah Pacy and Susan Chandler entered the court room and showed off their recovery. Amy Denny and Rose Cullender watched silently before turning their attention to the judge. He told them that he and the court were both satisfied with the verdict, and then solemnly sentenced them to be hanged.

After both women had rejected Sir Matthew Hale's adjuration to confess, they were hustled outside and bundled into an open horse-drawn cart for the thirty mile journey to Cambridge, there to await their execution. As they journeyed through villages and hamlets, people emerged from their cottages to jeer the condemned women. Sir Matthew Hale also departed for Cambridge that morning, his passage through the countryside being accomplished more agreeably in a horse-drawn stage.

Four mornings later, after a reprieve had been denied

them, Amy Denny and Rose Cullender, dressed as they had been throughout, shuffled forward on the scaffold. Few among the hundreds who witnessed their public execution mourned their death. A few moments later as their bodies swung at the end of the hangman's rope, the popular view was that goodness had triumphed over evil with the dispatch of the devil's two disciples.

The Lowestoft witches were tried during an age when witchcraft, its exposure and the subsequent trial and execution of its practitioners, occupied the attention not only of the judiciary, but of the church and parliament also.

The sorcerous practices of Amy Denny and Rose Cullender which culminated in their trial appear to have commenced in 1659 with the bewitching of the Durent children – Elizabeth and Ann of whom were named in the indictment.

During the intervening period it is likely that the services of a witch finder would have been engaged to gather additional evidence against the women. Criticised by many for the manner in which they earned a living, these individuals, the best known of whom in Suffolk was Matthew Hopkins, travelled the country with their assistants and for a fee unmasked witches, and if required testified at their trial.

When Amy Denny and Rose Cullender eventually stood in the dock at Bury St Edmunds an assortment of witnesses were to testify against them, the most academically prominent of whom was Doctor Thomas Browne of Norwich. A believer in witchcraft ('he who denies witchcraft is an atheist'), Brown did nothing to enhance his reputation among his colleagues during the trial. His damning testimony consisted almost entirely of hearsay and opinions. Nevertheless his testifying in his professional capacity no doubt impressed the jury and contributed to the conviction of Denny and Cullender.

Yet who prevailed upon Doctor Browne to appear in court? There was speculation that either the magistrates sitting with Sir Matthew Hale, or even Hale himself was responsible. Certainly Browne and Hale were undergraduates at Oxford together between 1626 and 1629, which may have fuelled the latter notion.

What of Sir Matthew Hale? History records that he was a deeply religious man who attended church regularly and set aside part of each day for prayer, although paradoxically he retained a belief in occultism and witchcraft. This juxtaposition of faith and superstition may explain the subjective and perverse judgements he sometimes arrived at in his court.

With its combination of occultism, theatricality and judicial prejudice, the trial of the Lowestoft witches was typical of such seventeenth-century inquisitions. The laws against witchcraft remained on the statute book until 1736. Perhaps by then there were vociferous demands for a posthumous pardon of 'The Lowestoft Two'?

References

A Trial of Witches at the Assizes held at Bury-St-Edmunds in the County of Suffolk on 10th March 1664 (See footnote.) *Taken by a person then attending the courts*.

Childers, H. *Romantic Trial of Three Centuries* (John Lane The Bodley Head, 1912)

Geis, G and Bunn, 1. *Sir Thomas Browne and Witchcraft. A Cautionary Tale of Contemporary Law and Psychiatry*. (Originally published in the *International Journal of Law and Psychiatry vol. 4,* pp. 1-11. USA 1981)

Hopkins, M. *The Discovery of Witches* (H W Hunt, Norwich, 1931. A facsimile of the original edition published 1667)

Hibbert, C. *The English: A Social History 1066-1945* (Grafton, 1987)

A Hank of Hair

Jean McConnell

Jean McConnell regularly contributes fiction to crime and women's magazines, and her stories appear in many anthologies. She began as an actress and then turned to writing, having a great success with her first play for television, *Haul for the Shore*. She has since written drama, serials and for series on television, as well as radio plays and documentaries on real-life crime. She has published twenty stage plays, and from time to time directs for the theatre. She is a member of the Crime Writers' Association, the Writers' Guild and the Society of Women Writers and Journalists.

'**Mum! Mum!** They're draggin' the river! An' guess what's come up? A dead man wiv two 'eads!'

It wasn't, actually. But even Sergeant Rutland got a nasty turn. A pathologist, at a quick glance, and a quick glance was quite enough thank you, would have pronounced 'drowning with bloat'.

Some mousy hair was attached to the victim in the normal way, but the other, the blonde locks, were entangled in the epaulet button of his jacket. When the man was hoisted out of the river it became obvious that the blonde hair was a wig.

It added interest, that wig. The police were not unaccustomed to hooking bodies out of Mettle Weir. It looked like any other little hiccup of the Wensum, although it had dangerous shelves of rock for unwary swimmers. But the wig was a novelty.

'It's real hair and there's the name of a Paris peruquier sewn inside,' said WPC Morris.

'How do you suppose it happened?' asked Angie from the switchboard.

'Well, he wasn't swimming because he was fully dressed – even had a waistcoat.'

'This weather?'

'Fell in maybe. Off the bank.'

'You can't there, it's too shallow at the edge.'

'Out of a boat? But they didn't find one.'

'Well, he couldn't have fallen in above the weir because he'd have been caught in the barrier. Isn't it odd?'

Policewoman Morris agreed. She glanced towards the Superintendent's office, suspecting much the same conversation was going on in there.

'Is he local?' asked Angie.

'They haven't identified him yet.'

By the end of the week he still wasn't identified. There was nothing in his tattered pockets but a piece of string, eighty-five pence and a plastic bag. He wasn't on anyone's file and no one had reported him missing.

'Shame,' said Angie, who was a popular girl herself. 'Well, that's the end of *him.'*

She was wrong, for the doctor had found fingermarks round the man's throat that he didn't like the look of at all.

Thus the dossier on the lonely man whose neck seemed to bear evidence of at least one acquaintance landed on the desk of Detective Chief Inspector Popkin. Detective Sergeant Angus Forsyth stood by as Popkin examined the deceased's meagre possessions, watching as his cigarette ash grew long and dropped on to his trouser legs. Accidentally Angus let escape a small sigh.

'Bored, Forsyth?' said Popkin. 'Don't dawdle about then. Get on to this wigmaker in Paris.'

Within an hour they had the name of the purchaser, a Madame Cornelius Hellas, whose address was The Meads, Mettleshed, near Fakenham.

Angus got on the phone and introduced himself to Angie.

The Meads, it seemed, was owned by a dentist with a practice in Wimpole Street. Sergeant Rutland made enquiries and rang back to say that Mrs Hellas was away and Mr Hellas was in London.

On your feet, Forsyth, thought Angus.

Cornelius Hellas was obviously a dental surgeon of some distinction. A retainer, several hundred years old, showed Popkin and Angus into a large waiting room pregnant with mahogany.

On the walls were numbers of certificates of merit and on a huge sideboard stood several silver cups. They were not trophies from tooth-pulling contests as Angus fancifully imagined, but for boxing, javelin-throwing and swimming. In the latter, it seemed, Hellas had once been an Olympic team member.

'Used to do a bit of this myself,' said Angus, with some envy.

A nurse hurried in. 'Mr Hellas is very busy,' she said.

'This is a police enquiry and I'd be obliged for a moment of his time,' said Popkin.

'Oh. I'll try and get him.'

A few minutes later a firm step approached. Cornelius Hellas had muscular shoulders, a short neck and trim waist. The white jacket enhanced his sunbronzed skin. His trousers and shoes had a casual elegance. Angus blushed for Popkin's cardigan.

'What is this?' asked Hellas. 'Is it urgent?'

'It was your wife we really wanted to contact, sir, but she seems to be away. Out of the country, I believe. So perhaps – just a few points you could tell us.'

'Willingly, but you must see it is not very convenient now and I have patients right through until eight.'

'Tomorrow?'

'I was planning to drive home tonight.'

'To Mettleshed? May we call on you there?'

'So far?'

'We'll be in the area anyway.'

'Oh, will you? Fine. Very kind of you to understand.' Hellas strode off.

'Back to the saltmine, Forsyth,' said Popkin.

Angus picked up the inspector's hat and carried it after him.

The two policemen travelled to Norfolk the next morning. Angus had scarcely ten minutes to captivate Angie, before being whisked off to The Meads. A girl in a green overall showed them into a flagged hall, where a flower arrangement in a copper bowl reflected itself in an oak chest.

'Well ye com' this way, plaise sorr,' said the girl, leading them out to a sunny terrace, where steps led down to a large swimming pool. It was tiled in ultramarine with a wide edge of pink marble. A Romanesque wall sheltered it, and beyond, a weeping ash verged the river.

A head rose from the water, emitting air with a seal-bellow. Cornelius Hellas made towards them with a stylish butterfly stroke. 'Good morning!' He drew himself over the side and slipped into a terry-towelling robe. He sent the girl scurrying off for refreshments.

Popkin fumbled in his brief-case. 'As you see, Mr Hellas, just an ordinary woman's wig. Could you confirm this is your wife's property?'

'It could be. She has wigs made in Paris. She is French, you know.'

'Has she more than one?'

'Oh, many. The same colour but dressed differently.'

'Has she mentioned losing one?'

'Not that I recall. Why?'

'It was found in the river.'

Hellas stared at Popkin. 'How extraordinary. Whereabouts?'

'Mettle Weir.'

Hellas waited. 'It was in the possession of this man,' said Popkin, holding out the photograph.

'I thought you said it was in the river?'

'They both were.'

'Mettle Weir?'

'Yes. Dead. Do you know him?'

Hellas looked at the photograph in silence. 'Yes,' he said at last. 'I believe I do. I'm sorry he came to that.'

'Who was he?'

'He used to work here. His name was Peter Bromley.'

'How long was he with you?'

'A year. An accident? Or was it suicide?'

'We don't think it was either, Mr Hellas.'

130

Hellas looked taken aback.

'When did he leave here?'

'I dismissed him a few months ago. He was pilfering.'

'Did you notify the police?'

'No. I considered losing his job punishment enough. I never did take to the man, but I'm sorry to hear he's dead.'

As Hellas spoke, Angus heard a noise from a window above. The maidservant, he thought? Now she's off to the kitchen with that juicy bit.

'But why should he have taken a woman's wig? Isn't that odd?'

'No, Inspector. Given his inclination.'

'I see.'

'He left here four months ago.'

'Do you know where he went?'

'He left no address and I've heard nothing of him since. Until now.'

'How did you come to engage him in the first place?'

'He was a steward on a cruise we took. Made himself very useful. It was my wife persuaded me to take him on. I confess we didn't investigate his background too closely. He certainly knew his job.'

'Would your other servants know anything more about him?'

'The cook is new. The maid might help, but I warn you she's a simple soul.'

'We'll have a word nevertheless.'

'Inspector, was he much run down?'

'His clothes were in a bad state. But then we don't know what he'd been up to, do you?'

The conversation turned to Hellas' wife. They'd been in Portugal together until two weeks before, when Hellas had returned to his practice and she'd gone on to Cannes.

'Which hotel?' queried Popkin.

'The Oceana.'

Angus made a note.

'Will she be back soon?'

'No. I shall join her again in a few weeks' time.'

Popkin gathered his belongings about him.

A word with the cook confirmed she had never known Peter Bromley. Returning to the hall, the policemen found Hellas talking to the maid. He urged her towards them with an encouraging pat, then left them. Her eyes were swimming as she glanced at the photograph, nodded and turned away with a shudder.

'True it is then, sorr. He's dead entoirely.' The tears started down her face.

Entoirely, thought Angus, glad to put that photograph away.

She buried her face in Angus' chest and wept bitterly on to his tie. 'Don't waste too much grief on him, my dear,' chirruped Popkin. 'He wasn't the best of men, it seems.'

'He wasn't the *worst!*' she said with spirit. 'And he wasn't a thief! Indeed he was not!'

It *had* been her at the window.

Her voice softened. 'And hadn't he the way with him? Ye'd need a heart of stone to keep him out of your bed.'

Angus looked at Popkin.

'An' now he's cold in his grave. An' I thinkin' I'd be hearin' from him any day, so.'

'Why? Where did you think he was?'

'Canada, of course.'

'Canada!'

'Have you an address?'

'I have not.'

'Do you know of any relatives or friends...'

'No. An' it's scattered they'd be, him bein' on the boats an' all. He said he would send for me.' She looked

132

crestfallen. 'Oh. I'm thinkin' he didn't mean a word of it. Well, it's all one now, rest his soul. But he'll never see the baby. An' I'd have liked foine to have shown it to him, when it comes.'

'*His* baby?'

'Whose else would it be? Ye think I'm a whore?' Her face crumpled again and she ran away down the passage, sobbing.

The police car speeded back to the station. 'And yet,' remarked Popkin, 'Hellas implied the man was effeminate. There seems to be a difference of opinion.'

'I'd say the girl's carried more weight,' said Angus.

'Why did he have that wretched wig?' worried Popkin.

'A keepsake from Mrs Hellas?' Angus was hardly serious, but Popkin turned his full attention on him. Angus always found this unnerving. It happened so seldom.

'In any event, I wonder if Mrs Hellas can throw more light on the matter.'

Angus' heart rose. Mrs Hellas... Cannes!

'By the way, you mislaid your hat, sir,' said Angus, handing it to Popkin with an engaging smile.

Next day, just when Angus had given up hope, Popkin sent for him. 'There's a flight for you at one-thirty, Forsyth. Pick up the ticket at the airport.' He handed a file of documents to Angus. 'She's at...'

'The Oceana Hotel,' prompted Angus.

'Use your charm, lad. It should come in for something. Make the most of your trip.'

'Yes, sir, I'll...'

'And be back here tomorrow morning.'

All tanned and set up for the winter, thought Angus.

'Madame Hellas? Ah oui! Elle est sur la plage, monsieur.'

The porter left Angus and Inspecteur Bitouzet in the

Oceana's foyer and, from the window, Angus watched him go down the hotel's private beach to where a couple lay on sunbeds with fingers entwined. He roused the woman and she accompanied him back with the young man following behind.

In the manager's office Angus was introduced to the woman whose hair was of that same silvery blonde as the wig from Mettle Weir.

She was surprised by the news of Bromley. 'How sad,' she said. 'He always worked well. It was unfortunate that he was not to be trusted.'

'How do you suppose the man came to be in possession of your wig, madam?' asked Angus.

'How should I know?'

'What made you employ him in the first place?'

'My husband hired him.'

'He says you persuaded him.'

She paused, then shrugged.

'Your husband thinks Bromley was homosexual.'

'I would not know.'

'You have no idea what he might have been doing these last months?'

'I have been away from England. My husband also. He had been overworking, so I shuttered the house and he went on a clay-pigeon shoot in Portugal, then I came on here.'

'Your maid said she thought he had gone to Canada.'

'Oh?'

'She says she is pregnant by him.'

Mrs Hellas showed only mild surprise, Angus noted. Maybe the Irish girl had been lying. Then he remembered the distraught little face. No, that wasn't it.

Angus checked some more notes that Popkin had required, then closed the interview. The lady either could not or would not tell him any more about Peter Bromley.

'A nice trip for you, uh?' she remarked, pleasantly.

'Too brief,' smiled Angus, glancing out of the window.

'Won't you have time to swim? The weather is so beautiful here.'

'It wasn't bad at home. In fact your husband was having a dip.'

'Oh, he swims any time.'

'Beautiful place, The Meads.'

'I hope it was in order. When one is away things get neglected.'

They had reached the foyer, where the young man stood waiting.

'I am sorry to have been so unhelpful, sergeant.'

'May I briefly retain your passport, madam?'

She sighed. 'Please leave it with the manager,' she said, and the young man shepherded her out into the sunlight.

'Madame's passport seems to be in order,' said Inspecteur Bitouzet.

'Nevertheless,' said Angus boldly,' that woman is not Mrs Hellas.'

Angus was not in such a hurry to commit himself to Popkin. He dialled his number, hung up again, bit his thumbs, nosed round the hotel, and finally donned his swim trunks and strode down to the beach where he stretched near to where Mrs Hellas lay with tiny plastic shields on her eyelids and nose. Beside her the young man now slept on his stomach.

Angus took a swim then, when he saw the woman sit up for a cigarette, he strolled up to the beach and paused beside her. 'You see,' he said, 'I couldn't resist it.'

She smiled up at him. 'You must get some oil.' Her eyes roved. 'Your skin is so fair.'

The young man did not stir, but his eyes were open now.

Angus sat down on his haunches, casually. 'The colour of that sea!' he said. 'Ultramarine. Beautiful.'

135

She leaned back. Her bracelet, heavy with gold charms, fell down her arm clinking and sparkling.

'Did you have it in mind when you made the pool at The Meads? I mean the colour of the tiles?'

'My husband designed that,' she said.

'Very artistic. And that green marble around the edge.'

She examined her cigarette as if afraid it had gone out. 'Yes,' she said. 'It is very pretty.'

'I've never seen green marble like that before. Lovely.'

She reached for the Ambre Solaire. The young man sat up. 'Oh. May I introduce Philippe Lalage,' she said.

The young man held out his hand. Angus made to shake it, but the woman started pouring sun lotion into it. His slim brown frame made Angus feel like a bed-bolster.

'Perfect setting by the river,' said Angus. 'What period is your house?'

'Several,' said the woman, and lay down to be massaged.

A few more pleasantries and Angus wished them good day.

At home, Popkin would just have his trotters in the trough. Quel dommage. Angus put a call through regardless.

'You think you ought to stay on,' quipped Popkin.

'No, sir, no.'

'Well?'

'It's not her, sir.'

'What?'

'I can't give you categorical proof, but...'

'Speak up, Forsyth.'

'It's things she said. And things she hasn't. She mentioned shuttering up the house. There weren't any shutters on The Meads, but they mostly close their properties that way over here. That's not all...'

'Glad to hear it.'

'I talked of green marble round the pool and she accepted

it. Who could forget they'd got pink marble? Must have cost a packet.'

'Don't mix your standards with hers.'

'No, sir. But she's never stayed at the Oceana before, and I couldn't find anyone who'd ever seen her and Hellas together.'

'Mm.'

'She looks younger than you'd expect. It's Jeanne Hellas' passport, but the franking on the photograph is blurred, I'd swear.'

'And that's it?'

'Well, yes, sir. But if she's Mrs Hellas, I'm Arnold Schwarzenegger.'

'Who?'

'Look, sir...'

'Forsyth.'

'Yes, sir?'

'Meet me off the first plane tomorrow at Nice airport.'

When Popkin arrived next day, Cornelius Hellas was beside him. He said little on the ride to the hotel, but when Angus pointed the woman out as she skimmed landward on water-skis, he frowned. 'No,' he said. 'That is not my wife!'

Popkin sent for the woman to be brought to the hotel office. She arrived looking angry.

'Madame Hellas?' asked Popkin, politely.

'Oui.'

'Voici Monsieur Hellas.'

Hellas stepped forward. 'Where is my wife? And why are you impersonating her, madame?'

The woman stared at him, then relaxed. 'So,' she said. 'You are Cornelius.'

'Why are you pretending to be my wife?'

'She asked me to. To give her time to get away.'

'Away? Away where?'

She shrugged. 'It was just a temporary arrangement.'

'How is it that you have her passport?' asked Popkin.

'Oh, that. Her friend arranged it all. He has many connections.'

'Her friend?' queried Hellas.

'You mean, madame...' Pipkin said.

'Rivet. Mademoiselle Annette Rivet.'

'You are saying Mrs Hellas has gone off with another man?'

'I regret, but yes.' She looked at Hellas. 'She was afraid you would stop her.'

'She was right!'

'So she asked me to stay here in her place. To post letters she had written and...'

'How long has she been gone?'

'Almost two weeks.'

'So she never came here at all?'

'Not to the Oceana, no.'

Hellas suddenly gripped her wrists. 'Where has she gone?'

'I do not know!'

'Who is the man?'

'He is Dutch. He loves her.'

'*I* love her!'

'She was afraid she would never go if she saw you again. I warned her it was unwise, but she convinced me.'

Hellas shook her arm so that the jewelled charms flashed. 'This persuaded you to help her, no doubt,' he said. He turned and strode out of the room distraught.

'I hope Monsieur Hellas will forgive his wife,' said Annette Rivet. 'A woman in love becomes a little mad, you know.'

Angus showed her out then sat down opposite his melting superior. It seemed they'd simply got themselves mixed up in a little domestic tickatoo.

Still, it *had* been Mrs Hellas' wig in the river.

'Give an eye to Mr Hellas,' suggested Popkin. Angus trailed after the man along the promenade on the directions of the hall porter. He passed under sunbathers with tortoise heads, perfect girls in Thai silk and young men wearing blue eyeshadow, finally spotting Hellas sitting in a bar. With Annette Rivet. Angus found a discreet place to watch from.

It was reasonable that Hellas should have sought her out to question her further, but there was something in their manner that seemed out of key. When the beach-boy suddenly arrived Angus saw Hellas stiffen, and when he put a hand on the woman's shoulder Hellas knocked it off angrily. The beach-boy, eyes blazing, pulled the woman to her feet. At which Hellas rose and landed a punch on the boy's jaw that sent him reeling.

Hellas marched off towards the Oceana. Angus followed.

Popkin agreed the scene had been odd. 'Oh well, leave it to the gendarmes, lad. Our business is with the murdered Peter Bromley.'

Then a call came for Popkin, and when he replaced the receiver he sat back with a weary sigh. 'My mistake,' he said. 'Our business is not Peter Bromley. Some clot jumped the gun. He wasn't murdered at all.'

'What? But the bruises...'

'Didn't account for death. Happened earlier, probably in a brawl. He wasn't killed. He just drowned.'

'But he couldn't have fallen in...'

'They're presuming suicide. So that's that.'

It was over. And yet – Angus was bothered by the loose ends.

In April, Angus happened to be working with Popkin again on the case of a young woman discovered in a leafy wood with her throat cut and her knees still open, who'd been food for maggots since the summer. They were interrupted by a caller. A Miss Maureen Doyle. The maid they'd seen at The Meads. Popkin put a folder over the photo on his desk as she came in.

'They told me I ought to seek you out to find did he leave any money, whatever,' she started.

'Who?'

'Peter. For the baby. It's come now. A girl, Fiona.'

'Very nice. Not sure we can help you though, my dear.'

'I'm stayin' at a hostel. An' some of 'em were sayin; maybe he'd money in the bank.'

'It wasn't possible for you to stay on at The Meads, then?'

'Sure he made a clean sweep! You'd never have thought herself would take to the hills like that.'

'Were they so happy together then?' asked Angus.

'Indeed not. Didn't they fight fit to make yer hair stand.'

'Then why is it so surprising?'

'Well, I'd swear she's not planned it. Let's hope she's happy for many times I've seen the swollen eye on her. An' I don't begrudge her the crumb of comfort she got from Peter, for Mr Hellas drove her to it, when it was him she really wanted all the time, so it was.'

All the stranger her going off, thought Angus.

The Irish girl rose. 'Well, it was just a chance. Peter would not have begrudged the baby inheritin' his money if he'd been alive.'

Angus led her downstairs.

'He used to take me dancin'. And to an Italian café. I'll do my best for his daughter, I will.' She walked off with a defiant little step. Into the sunset.

It was a surprise an hour later when the girl's voice smacked over the telephone at them. 'I've found him!'

'Who?'

'Peter Bromley! He's not dead at all, the divil!'

'Where is he?'

'In the Italian café. I walked past for old times' sake and who's sittin' in the window but himself! An' beside him this glitterin' little blonde!'

'Is he still there?'

'Not entoirely. That is, he's unconscious.'

'How...?'

'I hit him with a sauce bottle.'

'We're on our way,' said Angus. 'We'll collect the pair of you.'

In the police car returning, the Irish girl told Peter Bromley about the baby. He was surprised but not displeased. He gave her a cuddle.

Popkin and Angus studied the man. He certainly looked a little like the corpse. But not enough. Definitely not enough.

'Why do you suppose Hellas identified the victim as you?' asked Popkin.

'Search me.'

'Miss Doyle, surely you knew it wasn't Peter?'

'But Mr Hellas said the photo was of Peter and not nice to look at. So I didn't look too close.'

Popkin turned to Bromley. 'He might have known you'd turn up sooner or later and confound the whole story.'

'No. I was supposed to go to Canada for good, you see. But I only got as far as Dublin.'

'Sure, a man could mislay himself in Dublin,' accepted Maureen.

'Why did Hellas dismiss you?' asked Popkin suddenly.

'Well...' Bromley looked towards the girl.

'It was for pilfering, wasn't it?'

The man looked incredulous. 'Is that what he said?'

'Yes.'

'It figures. He wouldn't want to say I was having it off with his wife.'

141

'That was the real reason?'

'That was *his* reason.'

'You weren't?'

'No. Fact was, he treated her so rough she'd taken to the bottle and I used to smuggle her the odd jug. He cottoned we were up to something and presumed it was the usual.'

The policemen were inclined to believe him.

'Anyway, why all this fuss about Mrs Hellas' wig?' asked Bromley.

'It was a possible means of identifying the body.'

'Why don't you get on to *her?*'

'She's gone off with another man,' said Maureen.

'Never on your life, Maureen.'

'Well, that's what I thought. She left behind her jewels and things. And her little dog. She'd have sent for him, surely. It's too late now, Mr Hellas had him put down.'

Popkin looked interested. 'If she hasn't run off with a lover, where do you think she's got to?'

'Someone must have swept her off her feet.'

'Someone damn special to make her abandon The Meads. It's her property, after all. That's all he stuck to her for, I'd say.'

'And yet,' mused Popkin, 'Hellas seemed so upset at losing her.'

'Nah,' said Bromley. 'He'd have welcomed it.'

'I wonder why he never left *her,*' persisted Popkin.

'They lived in a fair old style, you know. And you don't kill the golden goose.'

I wonder, thought Angus.

'Anyway, it was that poor soul in Mettle Weir got killed,' said Maureen.

'And even he wasn't killed. He drowned,' corrected Angus.

'In any event it wasn't me, mate,' said Bromley cheerfully.

142

When the couple had gone, they checked if Mrs Hellas was still missing. She was.

'It wouldn't surprise me if he'd quietly exxed her out, sir.'

'But how? Where? Bodies are very difficult to dispose of, Forsyth, and don't you forget it.'

'No, sir.'

'Well, the least we can do is tell Hellas the good news about Bromley.'

'Yes, sir!'

'Meantime, try to check with the airlines on the exact day Hellas travelled back from Portugal and whether he was alone or not.'

Duly, Angus reported back. 'It was a night flight apparently, sir. And he brought with him excess luggage. A packing case. Declared as dental equipment.'

'Did Customs open it?'

'No idea, sir.'

'Didn't it occur to you it might have been Mrs Hellas?'

'It was only two feet square, sir.'

'*Part* of her?'

'I don't think so, sir. You see, she travelled back with him.'

Angus savoured Popkin's expression. But an hour later the Chief had discovered a bit of fat himself.

'He's on the move, Forsyth. After the money. He's been to her trustees demanding a settlement. I think we'll tiptoe up on him in Mettleshed.'

Angie flashed into Angus' mind. In a red sweater.

'Heard you were coming up,' said Angie, fluttering a forest of eyelashes. Angus made an assignation.

'Sorry to disturb the idyll, Forsyth,' said Popkin.

But it was nothing to the idyll they disturbed at The

Meads, beside the pool. The woman sat up with a gasp, pulling a towel about herself. It was Mademoiselle Rivet.

Hellas rose angrily, grabbing a towelling coat.

'Beg pardon, sir,' said Popkin. 'We rang and rang...'

'All right! What do you want?'

'Didn't know Miss Rivet was here with you.'

'Our acquaintance in Cannes developed.'

It did that, thought Angus.

'We tried to contact you in town, but they said you had a chill and were at home.'

'Shaking it off,' added Angus.

Told about Bromley, Hellas reacted calmly. 'The photograph looked like Bromley to me.'

It had to be a lie.

'We thought you'd like to know.'

'Very good of you to come specially. Very grateful.' He actually smiled. Patronisingly. A mistake.

'About your wife's wig,' said Popkin. 'We still wish to identify the dead man, you understand. It would be nice to talk to her about it.'

'My dear man, she's probably the other side of the world by now.'

'No. We've reason to believe she's in this country, sir.'

Annette Rivet emerged from the changing room in an elegant wrap. Hellas lowered his voice. 'Please Inspector, be discreet! I plan to marry Mademoiselle Rivet. Have you news of my wife? Has she come back?'

'Really Hellas, she came back with you from Lisbon – eight months ago. The airline has a record.'

'Of course it has. She intended to come but changed her mind, so I handed in the ticket.'

You had to admire the man.

'You seem to think I know where my wife is, Inspector.'

'You'll admit it's odd there being no news of her whatever.'

144

'She's left me for another man. That's not police business, is it? You'd never have known she'd gone if that man's body hadn't been found with her wig tangled up with it.'

'That's true, sir,' said Popkin humbly.

'But it's a blessing in disguise for me.' He took the woman's hand and kissed it. She hadn't said a word throughout. And with Hellas holding her fingers in a grip turning her knuckles white, she wasn't likely to.

'Will you be here tomorrow if anything comes up, sir?'

'What do you mean – comes up?'

'Concerning the dead body, of course.'

On the way back to the police station Popkin dropped his cigarette ash fitfully about the car. 'Did he kill her here, or on the Continent? Did he kill her at all? Let's suppose he did.'

'Yes, sir.'

'Didn't take him long to change his attitude to Miss Rivet. Do you think he set up the whole Cannes drama for our benefit?'

'He's certainly sitting pretty now, sir. With his wife's lovely old property and a lovely new woman to put in it.'

'In clover,' agreed Popkin. 'We shall be staying the night in Mettleshed.'

That evening Popkin started more local enquiries about Mrs Hellas, but Angus was free to wrestle happily with Angie in the back row of the cinema.

Next morning Popkin had unearthed a jobbing gardener with useful things to tell them.

'I was sittin' watchin' for this fox, you see boy. 'Ad three chicken nigh afore. 'Bout two in the mornin' 'twas. An' this car come by, the Mercedes with Mister Hellas drivin'. It turned in the gate an' I saw Mrs H. sittin' up there 'side 'im.'

'But she was never seen in the house. You're sure?'

'Sure as day, boy. Moon was up, see.'

'Why didn't you tell anyone before?'

'Nobody ast afore.'

'But you surely heard she was supposed to have run away?'

'None of my business, be it.'

'You couldn't have mistaken the woman?'

'Me! Shot the fox from twenty yard.'

It added weight.

'Do we take the place apart, sir?' asked Angus.

'Might not be necessary,' said Popkin. But when they left he had a search warrant stuffed in his bulging pockets. And there was a sturdy constable accompanying them.

There were suitcases in the hall at The Meads. By the pool the couple were studying maps.

'Planning another trip, Mr Hellas?'

'Mademoiselle Rivet's vacation ends tomorrow.'

Popkin told Hellas the gardener's story. 'He's positive it was your wife,' he concluded.

'Where is she, then? Hiding under the bed?'

'Do you mean the rose bed, Mr Hellas?'

'Don't be ridiculous!' He turned to the young woman. 'This is too boring, chérie. Take your swim.'

Obediently the woman slipped into the water. But she remained within earshot.

'Your wife is dead and you know it.'

'If that's true, I'm glad!'

'That's more like it.'

'She is of no interest to me any more.'

'But her money is.'

'My wife is very rich. If *I* had deserted *her* she would have expected maintenance!'

'What happened that night, Mr Hellas? The night you returned from Portugal.'

'She was not with me!'

146

'Did you get a little too rough with her for once? Where did it happen? Indoors? Such a lovely old house. Are there wall cavities? A priest hole?'

'You can pull every bloody inch apart! You have no evidence against me! You've built this whole fiction out of a piece of frippery!'

'Oh yes.' Popkin produced the wig from his pocket. 'What an oversight. But with these expensive ones you don't know when they're being worn and when they're not. Eh?'

'I don't have to answer these questions, Popkin. But call me to the station and I'll bring my solicitor. Just get off my property! I won't have you frightening Mademoiselle Rivet.'

'I'm not surprised she's frightened. Does she know what she's letting herself in for?'

'We shall be married as soon as I'm free.'

'You're already free, Mr Hellas. It was but the work of a moment, as they say. Did she struggle? How was it? Anaesthetic, the dentist's special? Or a stocking? That's a perennial. Oh no, I see it all. A midnight swim!'

A gasp came from Annette Rivet nearby.

'Can't you see it? A race to the deep end. You're a swimmer, Forsyth, how would you do it?'

'I'd get my legs round her, sir. Then maybe pull her feet upwards'

The woman whimpered.

'Quite wrong, Inspector!' barked Hellas.

'Oh? She didn't struggle, sir? She was unconscious? But where do you put the body, Forsyth? That's the problem.'

'I think you load it down and pop it in the pool, sir.'

'Ah! Take a peep up the deep end, mademoiselle, will you?'

'It is the English sense of humour, chérie.'

'But how long would it take for the wig to come loose, sir?' asked Angus.

147

'It didn't come loose, Forsyth. It got tangled up in a drowning man's fingers. And they drifted up together. Like this.'

Popkin threw the wig into the pool. The dead hair spread out beside the woman. She screamed and pushed it away. The wig undulated towards her. She screamed again, gulped water and began to flounder.

Hellas jumped in beside her. But she backed away from him frantically, striking at his face and shrieking, 'Assassin!'

Hellas grabbed her by the throat.

Angus dived flat between them. He aimed his feet into Hellas' stomach. The water softened the impact but Hellas released the woman's neck. Angus thrust her towards the side, then turned to fend off Hellas who was lunging at him.

They were matched for size, but Hellas caught at the waist of Angus' trousers and hoisting himself upwards, flung himself spreadeagled over the policeman, bearing him to the bottom. His knee was in Angus' groin and his elbow on his Adam's apple.

Fainlights! thought Angus. Any minute his brains were going to pour down his nose. And his chest would split open like a peascod, letting his ribs fly out. The ultramarine water turned red then roaring black.

None too soon the weight lifted off him. Angus fought to the surface and took in a great gasp of air. He paddled feebly to the side.

The woman was lying on the pink marble, unconscious. Hellas was in the hands of a dripping constable.

Angus felt his mind clearing. Rinsed clean. He saw it all. Hellas explaining about the wig. Connecting it with Bromley. Sending the police off in the wrong direction. Instead of what should have been the obvious one – to the bottom of the river! He staggered over to Popkin.

'Sir! Mettle Weir! We must drag it again.'

148

'I've arranged to do it after lunch, Forsyth.'

She was there, of course. Her naked body wedged under a shelf of rock. A task for a strong swimmer. An Olympic champion.

It took the frogmen twenty minutes to dislodge her. She wouldn't have come up again in a hurry. Would have rotted away unregarded, if that lonely man hadn't caught at her in his drowning panic.

The canvas bundle was being trundled up the bank when a shabby figure stepped out from behind a tree. His face was troubled.

'Do you know who it is?' he asked.

'Why?'

'Do you? It's important, honest.'

'How do you mean?'

'Well, you see last time I was round 'ere, few months ago, there was this chap. Bit daft. Come from the Norf, I fink. We 'ad a scrap an' I smashed 'is specs, din' I?'

'Who was he?'

'Dunno. On the road. Like me.'

'You left him here by the river?'

'Yah. Seein' that body give me a turn. 'E was blind wivout 'is specs. Wouldn't like to fink 'e wandered in and drownded.'

The tramp's mild little eyes were anxious.

'Don't worry, lad,' said Popkin. 'This isn't his body. It's a woman.'

The man heaved a sigh of relief, saluted cheerfully and shuffled away.

No, thought Angus. This isn't his body. Not *this* one.

Killing Little William

Carole Rawcliffe

Carole Rawcliffe was Born in London, but raised in Norwich in 1965. [illegible] for many years, [illegible] Burden of History, her Research in General History now works at the Centre of East Anglian Studies in the University of East Anglia, where she is building the history of the Great Hospital, Norwich, and working towards an [illegible] history. Her most recent book, Medicine and Society in Later Medieval England appears in the Spring of 1995.

Carole Rawcliffe is a medieval historian who moved to Norwich in 1992, after working for many years at the Institute of Historical Research in London. She is now based at the Centre of East Anglian Studies at the University of East Anglia, where she is writing the history of the Great Hospital, Norwich, and teaching early medieval history. Her most recent book, *Medicine and Society in Later Medieval England,* appears in the spring of 1995.

William's mutilated body was discovered on Easter Saturday in a wood on the outskirts of Norwich. The victim, a naive and unusually obedient child of twelve, had disappeared five days earlier with a man who claimed to be the archdeacon's cook and had offered him pocket money to help in the kitchens.

Against her better judgement, the youngster's mother had let him go, but it soon became clear that the stranger was not what he had seemed. Some of her relatives maintained from the outset that he had been bribed to procure victims for a gang of child-molesters, and before long extraordinary rumours were circulating in the city. Yet none of these allegations could be substantiated by hard fact or even circumstantial evidence, and no reliable witnesses came forward to testify.

So there matters rested for a few years, until the arrival in Norwich of a private investigator in holy orders, who was not only convinced that abuse of the worst kind had taken place, but actually set out to prove that the boy had been crucified in a gruesome parody of the Easter ceremonies held in his own church.

Some people laughed at the idea, and there were even sceptics among the clergy. In the end, however, his single-minded determination to expose what he believed to be a network of anti-Christian conspirators proved sufficiently strong to convince those in authority, with tragic consequences for the accused and their families.

How familiar this story seems. Hardly a week goes by in the England of the 1990s without some discussion of ritual abuse and the methods used to detect it in the popular press or on television. At present the debate remains as heated as ever: experts still cannot agree on the best means of collecting, evaluating and interpreting the evidence; and many reject the very idea as little short of fantasy. Young

William's murder raised similar issues, and although we now have only limited information about the case it provides a salutary warning of how easily fear, prejudice, religious extremism and a self-seeking desire for publicity can turn supposition into fact and fact into persecution. Such is human nature, and so it was when King Stephen occupied the throne over eight hundred years ago, and the boy met his death.

The Life and Passion of William the Martyr of Norwich, our only contemporary account of the crime, was begun in about 1150 by a Cathedral monk named Thomas of Monmouth. He had only just joined the Benedictine community there and was immediately gripped by the story of the murder, which had taken place some six years earlier, in 1144. Even in a society used to sudden and violent death, the child's youth and the unmistakable marks of torture found on the body had caused widespread outrage. It was assumed in certain quarters that only the Jews (a group vindictively stigmatised by the Church as a byword for inhumanity) could have perpetuated such a cruel deed, but no proof had been forthcoming. As was often the way, interest in the affair soon began to fade, and within a matter of months speculation more or less ceased.

Thomas's mission, as he saw it, was to bring those responsible to justice by unearthing the necessary evidence. Having thus established the complicity of the Jews he could reveal William in all his glory as a holy martyr. For to him the boy was no accidental victim of perversion or brutality, but a saint predestined by God to suffer torment and death at the hands of the infidel, and to undergo, through crucifixion, the very same fate as Christ himself.

This was a large claim, which the monk confidently sought to uphold through the meticulous and systematic presentation of new information, culled from interviews with the surviving relatives, with key witnesses who had failed to come forward at the time, and with the priests or confessors of others since dead. In some instances, he argued, fear had prevented people from speaking out; one or two had been bribed to keep silent; and a few had even forgotten salient facts. Most important of all, heaven was on his side as he fought to expose the truth.

Thomas was assiduous in his labours, although unlike his fictional contemporary, Brother Cadfael, the outcome of his detective work was predetermined from the start. No element of doubt, no twinge of uncertainty could be permitted to cloud his judgement or query the attribution of guilt.

Most medieval Christians believed devoutly in the miraculous power of saints and relics. In an age before the invention of the microscope and almost all the other major scientific advances which today make medicine and surgery reasonably effective, the sick generally had recourse to prayer and pilgrimage as well as physic. The restricted nature of the winter diet meant that many seasonal ailments, such as scurvy, went into remission once the pilgrimage season began in spring and fresh food became available, although since they had no knowledge of vitamins those concerned naturally ascribed their improvement to supernatural causes.

A church or cathedral with a healing shrine, such as that at Bury St Edmunds, could attract vast crowds bearing gifts of money, plate and jewels, so there was a strong economic as well as spiritual motive for the monks at Norwich, who as yet had no visible relics, to acquire some of their own. The competition was certainly fierce. Already, in the spring of 1144, on learning that little William had *perhaps* been murdered by the Jews and might *possibly* qualify as a martyr, the abbot of St Pancras's Abbey in Lewes, Sussex, had put in a bid for the body.

'No sum of money would have induced him to allow of it being taken elsewhere,' we are told, 'but that he would have kept him with the utmost diligence as his most precious treasure.' Wisely, the Bishop of Norwich refused to part with the corpse and had it exhumed for reburial in the monastic cemetery, although he still nursed serious reservations about William's posthumous value. Nor was he alone.

When preparing his initial report on the circumstances of the murder (which forms the first section of his book), Brother Thomas expressed justifiable concern lest his version of events be called into question, if not openly ridiculed. Much of what he recorded was already public knowledge, and gives a rough idea of the facts as established in 1144; but his introduction of new, hitherto undisclosed evidence implicating the Jews in a sophisticated international network of ritualised murder must have seemed implausible to some readers.

Far more took exception to the extravagant claims now being made on behalf of 'a poor neglected, ragged little fellow', whose short life might have been pathetic but showed few signs of incipient sanctity. Perhaps this was why Thomas assumed a defensive tone, protesting that 'I would fain not be called a falsifier by the ill-disposed, or an inventor of lies... as if I were spreading absurd fictions.'

Even so, he still got off to a controversial start by recounting a vision allegedly vouchsafed by God to the boy's mother, Elviva, when she was pregnant in 1132. The alarming news that her as yet unborn child would be martyred once he reached the age of twelve produced a somewhat muted response, for like so many other protagonists in the drama (or at least this version of it), she was plagued by a defective memory, forgetting for the best part of two decades to mention what must have been a profoundly disconcerting experience.

Curiously, too, anxiety about William's safety had not prevented her from arranging for him to leave home as an apprentice skinner when he was eight (which was not unusual), nor had she felt it prudent to decline the stranger's offer of employment, made at such a risky period in his short life.

Until then, William had lodged in Norwich under the watchful eye of his uncle, Godwin Sturt, whose concern about his association with Jewish customers seems to have been real enough. Soon after the murder, Godwin had publicly accused them of butchering his nephew, and demanded justice before the bishop. But he could only make the vaguest references to 'proof', which, in the event, hinged upon a dream in which God had warned his wife that the Jews would tear off one of her limbs.

Despite the current strength of anti-Semitic feeling in England and the confidence placed in signs and omens, dreams were inadmissible as evidence in a court of law. 'Forasmuch as that which you affirm to be certain is so far clearly uncertain to us,' warned the bishop, 'we shall at any rate take care to arrive at a certain knowledge of this business.'

It is thus hard to believe that evidence from Godwin's own daughter, linking the Jews with William's mysterious new master, could have remained hidden for another six years. She had, it transpired, been instructed by her mother to follow the boy when he left home for the last time, and had watched as he was handed over to his persecutors. Why had none of this been mentioned in 1144, when Godwin was desperate to prove his case against the Jews? Had the girl also succumbed to amnesia, unlocked only by Brother Thomas's skilful questioning? Or had her childhood recollections become genuinely confused by her parents' version of the crime?

Fear rather than forgetfulness had evidently prevented another witness from testifying, although Thomas was now able to produce her statement with a flourish, like an ace hidden up his sleeve.

That William had been cruelly tormented, with a wooden gag, or teazle, thrust into his mouth, knotted ropes tied tightly about his head and neck and signs of scalding on his body, was never in any doubt. The corpse had, however, already been exposed for three days before it was discovered, had then been buried where it lay in unconsecrated ground, dug up soon afterwards for inspection by Godwin and reburied again for another month before the bishop ordered a proper interment. Even allowing for the limitations of current medical knowledge, any informed assessment of William's other injuries was clearly out of the question, and had never been attempted at the time. In fact, his earthly remains were initially treated with a casual indifference which suggests that not even his nearest and dearest were at all bothered about them.

Thomas of Monmouth none the less felt able to assert that, like Christ, the young saint had been forced to wear a crown of thorns and had been wounded in the side by a sharp weapon. Since the Jews were far too cunning to implicate themselves by piercing both hands and feet with nails, the apparent absence of wounds on all four extremities could be explained, although such a negative line of reasoning clearly left much to be desired.

What the monk really needed to clinch his argument and make good the lack of specific details in Godwin's testimony was a witness to the crucifixion itself. His prayers were answered. After six years' silence a Christian servant girl who had worked for one of the leaders of the Jewish community suddenly stepped forward. Her master, Eleazar, had been killed in about 1146 by the retainers of a Norman knight to whom he had loaned large sums of money, and being safely dead and buried could now be maligned with impunity.

Since his murderers had sought to escape prosecution by

protesting that the Jews had never been brought to book for little William's death, we may reasonably ask why the girl had not seized this opportunity to unburden herself. If she had been too terrified to speak while Eleazar was still alive (which, in view of the small size and vulnerable position of the Jewish enclave, is highly unlikely), there was now every reason to set the record straight. Given the enormity of what she claimed to have seen, such prolonged reticence seems quite astonishing, although Brother Thomas happily accepted that her fear of becoming unemployed and losing unpaid wages would, indeed, have persisted until he arrived on the scene three or four years later.

She then described, for the very first time, how Eleazar had ordered her to bring a bucket of boiling water to the room in which the child was being tortured (so he could wash the body and remove all the blood), and how she had seen his hapless victim through a chink in the door. With great presence of mind she had retained a belt and other possessions allegedly taken from the boy, and at long last she produced them as evidence.

She was, moreover, able to show Thomas the scene of the crime. Notwithstanding the perishable nature of medieval plaster work, distinctive marks indicated clearly that a post or stake had been attached to the wall of the secret chamber. And once again the Jews had been too crafty to leave any traces of a crucifixion!

Even better, from the investigative point of view, a renegade Jew named Theobald, who had recently converted to Rome and become a monk, revealed that every year a designated Jewish community undertook to revenge itself on 'the enemy' by sacrificing a Christian at Passover; and that in 1144 the lot had fallen on Norwich.

Although he claimed to be exposing a complex and institutionalised machinery for ritual murder known to each and every Jew in Europe, no other writings of the period, however biased, even hint at what would have been an explosive news item. Long familiarity with Jewish rites and ceremonies enabled him to supply the kind of authentic detail which could lend verisimilitude to any tall story; and this was, of course, all Thomas really wanted.

Theobald's voice may be heard at other points in the narrative, too, where he assumes a multiple identity as 'the Jews'. This otherwise anonymous source is credited by Brother Thomas with supplying unsavoury details about the murder, even to the extent of repeating some melodramatic exchanges over the best means of disposing of the body. We can only guess at Theobald's motives in turning against his own people: perhaps he had been expelled from their ranks, or had been overcome by the zeal of the convert. Quite possibly his commitment to the monastic ideal had been called into question, and he was anxious to win over his superiors.

His testimony proved to be a cornerstone in the ambitious edifice now under construction, but there were still some gaps in the brickwork, notably with regard to the conduct of the sheriff, John de Chesney, during the weeks after William's death.

As the officer responsible for the enforcement of law and order in Norwich, de Chesney had placed himself unequivocally on the side of the Jews in 1144, arguing that the bishop had no authority over them, and offering them a safe haven in the castle when it looked as if matters might turn violent. Since his first duty lay towards the King, whose special protection extended (at a price) to all English Jewry, de Chesney had no choice but to uphold their legal rights and the financial interests of his royal master, but to Brother Thomas his behaviour seemed suspicious, if not sinister. True to form, his enquiries revealed a cover-up of major proportions, involving not only the sheriff, who had died in 1146, but also one of the richest and most powerful citizens of Norwich.

While prostrate on his deathbed, three years later, terror at the thought of eternal damnation evidently prompted Aelward Ded to confess a fearsome sin. When passing Thorpe Wood, sunk in prayer, on Good Friday 1144, he had encountered two shifty-looking Jews on horseback. Although he did no more than touch the sack which one of them was carrying, he realised at once that it contained a human body. Yet when he galloped off in panic through the trees he at once resumed his private devotions and told nobody about the incident.

The Jews, who had been caught red-handed with little William's corpse, did not, however, appreciate their good fortune in meeting such a reticent soul. Instead of keeping quiet, they sought out the sheriff, to whom they offered an enormous bribe in return for help. Far from pocketing the money and then betraying their secret, as most officials in his position would have done, de Chesney kept his word. Firstly he forced Aelward to swear an oath of silence, and then he used his influence to hush up the whole affair.

Of all the dubious and often inconsistent statements collected by Brother Thomas in the course of his investigations, Aelward's confession seems particularly hard to credit. Would such a responsible and high-minded individual have failed to report what looked like a serious crime as soon as he reached Norwich? Would the Jews ever have entrusted a member of the ruling elite with information of this kind, let alone on the most sacred day of the Christian calendar? And significantly, would Aelward have continued to shoulder his oppressive burden of guilt for three more years after de Chesney's death? More to the point, we might profitably ask if he actually admitted any of these things, or if the words were posthumously ascribed to him by his confessor, in an attempt to shore up the case against the Jews.

It can hardly be coincidental that the priest concerned was an enthusiastic supporter of the cult now starting to form around little William's remains, and had himself begun to collect evidence of any reported miracles. The experiences of a young virgin from Dunwich, who had been rescued from the (apparently) unwelcome attentions of a fiendishly handsome incubus after praying to the boy martyr, gave him particular cause for rejoicing and were duly passed on to Brother Thomas for inclusion in the second part of his book. This was composed in about 1155, by which time William's body had been moved first to the chapter house of the Cathedral and then, in recognition of his growing fame, to a tomb beside the high altar.

Yet despite his heroic efforts as the child's propagandist and champion, which redoubled after a series of visions, early in 1150, commanding him to set up a proper shrine, Brother Thomas never quite managed to convince the sceptics.

Even his own prior had objected to the lavish decoration of the chapter house tomb, although the press of hopeful pilgrims and protests by many of the monks obliged him to concede Thomas's demands that the carpets, candles and other ornaments should be restored. Not surprisingly, his sudden death, a few months later, was reported smugly as an act of divine retribution, yet the unbelievers still mocked, and critics continued to pick holes in Brother Thomas's evidence. Exasperated by 'their saucy insolence and insolent sauciness', he decided to marshal all the information at his disposal, confounding his detractors with a display of irrefutable logic.

In his original version of events, the facts as understood in 1144 had been embellished with circumstantial detail, and the testimonies recorded later carefully woven into the narrative to form a seamless, persuasive whole. He now tried a different approach, itemising each piece of evidence in sequence, to present an overwhelming case against the Jews. His repeated insistence upon their innate wickedness and constant recourse to bribery (which may sometimes have been their only means of coping with a cruelly repressive legal system) suggests a desire to trick out his case by appealing to popular prejudice. Being quite devoid of any sense of humour, especially where little William was concerned, he not only failed to appreciate the ironic wit of those Jews who chided their Christian neighbours for want of gratitude at the generous gift of a brand new saint and martyr, but actually recorded their asides as further proof of guilt.

Brother Thomas added five more sections to his book, the last of which was completed in about 1173. These catalogue all the miracles attributed to William after the third translation of his remains, and undoubtedly helped to promote a short-lived but extraordinarily enthusiastic cult. From then onwards, however, interest began to wane and for the rest of the Middle Ages Norwich's boy 'saint' exercised no more than a strictly local attraction. He was, in fact, never canonised; and like so many other holy men, women and children held up for veneration during this period, soon lost his appeal as memories began to fade and his hold on the popular imagination diminished.

In this respect, Thomas's work as a publicist was not destined to last. But it continued to exert a pernicious influence in other areas, helping to fan the flames of anti-Semitism throughout Europe. So far as we can tell, the myth of the ritual sacrifice of Christian children by Jews originated in Norwich in 1150 as a result of one man's fanatical obsession. It soon spread on a wave of hysteria across England and France, with increasingly horrific consequences.

In retrospect, the Jews of Norwich were lucky to escape the fate of their co-religionists in Lincoln, where the discovery of the body of a nine-year-old boy down a well, in 1255, resulted in allegations similar to those made by Brother Thomas. Nineteen Jews were executed and many others were imprisoned in London until crippling fines had been paid. Here too the child was venerated as a saint and martyr, while the Jews, soon to be expelled from England altogether, came in for vilification and abuse.

We will never know who killed poor little William, or Hugh of Lincoln, or any of the other children whose deaths were blamed upon the Jews. If, as seems probable, William was murdered by the stranger who took him away on 20 April 1144, then his assailant must have been a Christian. No Jew could possibly have posed as the archdeacon's cook, or have gained the confidence of William's mother. Nor would Godwin Sturt, a notorious anti-Semite, have failed to mention that this nephew had last been seen in such unwelcome company. Or did he himself molest the boy? One thing is certain: another dangerous criminal might then have been found miles away, contemplating the joys of heaven in a monastic cloister. Brother Thomas was a very guilty man.

Readers who would like to learn more about this incident will find an English version of the original Latin chronicle in *Thomas of Monmouth, The Life and Miracles of St William of Norwich,* edited by A Jessopp and M R James (Cambridge, 1896). M D Anderson's book, *A Saint at Stake: The Strange Death of William of Norwich 1144* (London, 1964) and an article by G I Langmuir, 'Thomas of Monmouth: Detector of Ritual Murder' in volume 56 of the historical journal *Speculum* (1984), pp. 820-856, provide further background.

Listeners

Margaret Moore

Margaret Moore was born and educated in Northern Ireland, and has held a variety of posts in health, educational and commercial settings. Since 1979 she has lived in Cambridge. She is the author of four novels in the Harper Collins *Crime Club* series.

'**No more questions,** Dr Baxter? May I assume I've convinced you?' Matt Siddons raised one sandy eyebrow and twinkled, like a world-weary don wrapping up a seminar. Two Cromwellian past Masters of Princes' College glowered oilily from the wall above his head.

Our prisoner, woman, they warned. *Leave Cambridge University scandals to Cambridge men.* After fifteen minutes of Siddons' company I was tempted to obey. Only loyalty to an old schoolmate in need glued me to a Chippendale chair and the task in hand. The schoolmate was Ellen Adlethorpe M.Sc., CBE, sometime high-flying UN bureaucrat, now the first Mistress of Princes' in the college's five-hundred-year history.

You're such a good listener, Sarah. True, I'd had plenty of practice, as a family doctor, a policeman's wife and for the past year the host of a radio phone-in series. But sniffing the narcissus-scented breeze that drifted up from the First Court that Friday evening, I ached for my neglected garden.

'You've convinced me you accepted an anonymous bribe here in '85,' I said formally. 'As the price of your confession to an attempted rape.'

'My *false* confession.' The donnish façade cracked briefly. 'Why else should they—'

'Jury's still out on that one, far as I'm concerned. But I'll do what Ellen asked, none the less. When do you hope to start interviewing?'

'Tomorrow at tea-time. This is truly kind, Dr Baxter. Never miss your show when I'm on the road. No one I'd rather have as my minder.'

I winced. 'You do realise that I'll be acting as Mrs Adlethorpe's rep and on her terms?'

'No harassment, no walkabouts? Natch. Premature publicity wouldn't suit my book. Sorry – no pun intended.'

Siddons' smirk belied his disclaimer. He'd clearly every

intention of underscoring that morning's ultimatum to Ellen Adlethorpe. It was the last Friday of the Easter vacation, and few students or staff were in residence. The first reunion of the graduates of '84 and '85 was due to begin the following afternoon. A reunion of special significance, for Princes' had been an all-male institution until October 1981, and the first cohort of women students had graduated three years later.

Siddons had presented himself at the Mistress' Lodge with the declared purpose of investigating certain events which had occurred in May '85. Events which had prompted him to abandon his posts as Fellow Commoner in Creative Writing and part-time supervisor of candidates for the English tripos. Three questions preoccupied him. Who'd committed the crime he'd been accused of? Who'd put up £20,000 to buy him off, and with what motive?

The gatecrasher had requested Ellen's permission to interrogate past students and staff of his choice on college premises. Granted such access, he'd write up his findings in sober documentary vein. Denied it, he'd feel free to publish a Cambridge-based novel already in typescript. A poisonous fricassee of near-fact and gossip, Ellen surmised, in the vein of his much-hyped best-seller, *An Adman's Adventures in Tellyland.*

For Siddons had long since abandoned high art for quick profits, and from what I'd heard on the London media grapevine, he wasn't to be trusted. But I'd spared my friend this assessment at our hastily-arranged dinner that evening.

Ellen, who'd surfed through many a Prefects' mutiny and international crisis, was spilling Perrier over her bread rolls. 'My best hope is damage limitation. Whatever Siddons prints will spell trouble for the college in general and our women graduates in particular.'

I couldn't argue with her prognosis. For Siddons' alleged victim had been Rebecca Voysey, in death and in the last years of her short life, the most celebrated of the graduates of '85. As the star of a live TV talk show, *Becky Bites,* she'd earned a reputation for making or breaking the careers of the upwardly mobile. Her kittenish face dominated the news-stands. Her off-camera exploits rated huge print fonts, none huger than those announcing her drug-induced death last January.

SHOCK NEWS, the headlines had screamed. A shock to the star's dimmer fans, maybe, but hardly to her friends. And Voysey had had friends in unlikely places.

'*Will* you help, Sarah?' Ellen urged in the earnest tones I recalled from her Head Girl period. 'It's asking a lot, but as Richard's away...'

With my husband up north on a buying trip for his newly acquired antiques business, I'd counted on long therapeutic sessions of sowing, planting and potting-on. I yearned for a let-out. 'The man's timing sticks in my craw. After all these years...'

'He said Rebecca had implicitly released him from his undertaking by inviting him on to her show.'

'She did that?'

'Last December. A February date was agreed by Siddons' agent. The letters he showed me looked kosher.'

And Rebecca had overdosed in January. 'Did he expect her to wash dirty linen on air?'

'Mm-hm. He'd no proof. But it'd be in her character, wouldn't you say? I never willingly watched *Becky Bites* after my first sampling, but the show was standard after-dinner entertainment at lots of my friends' houses.' Ellen's Greek nose wrinkled. 'Competitive exhibitionism was the name of the nasty game, wasn't it? *I'll show you mine, you show me yours,* metaphorically speaking. That's how she got results.'

'Maybe so. What little I saw of Rebecca over crowded

rooms didn't suggest she'd be nice to know. She self-destructed messily. But Siddons—'

'Should let her rest in peace? Agreed. But the fact is he won't. And no one involved in the '85 business emerges with credit. I don't care tuppence about Siddons' reputation, but it's my duty to safeguard the college's. There must be no hint of a cover up. I owe that much to the Fellows who voted for my appointment – it was a braver step than I realised at the time – and to Ronnie Coombes.'

Ellen's housekeeper hove into view, bearing a tureenful of delicately scented vichyssoise.

'Lady Veronica Coombes?' I prompted when we were left to our own devices.

'The same. As Sir Desmond was Master from '81 to '85, I invited Ronnie to the reunion. She'll be staying at the Lodge, so she'll have to be told what Siddons is up to. Horrid for her.'

Unless perhaps the life peer, international do-gooder and BBC governor was better informed on the events of '85 than either of us? When I'd spotted Lady Veronica shepherding a spaced-out Rebecca Voysey out of a TV awards junket last December, I'd assumed she was acting as an old-style guardian of British Broadcasting morals. But Ellen's words had reminded me of a second link between those unlikely sisters.

'Have you told anyone except me about Siddons' ultimatum?'

'Only Ambrose Oates, the Senior Bursar. He's a poppet – one of my closest chums among the fellows. Besides, he's the sole member of the 1985 Disciplinary Committee still in post. A tight-lipped bunch, he assures me.'

'Was there evidence of attempted rape?'

'Injuries consistent with, according to Rebecca's doctor, who made an oral report to the committee. Neck-bites,

170

Ambrose thinks. Nothing major – and the doctor's dead now. If photographs were taken, they're not in the committee file.'

'Why weren't the police involved?'

'Rebecca made a statement to the Master and agreed to the medical exam on the understanding that the committee would treat both as confidential. She claimed that the trauma of a court appearance would wreck her Tripos chances.'

'And her doctor went along with this?'

'Apparently. Likewise Pip Mallow – the student friend who reported the incident to the Master. She's married now, and registered for the reunion.'

'So what *was* Voysey after? Compensatory cash?'

'If so, the Master didn't let on to the Disciplinarians. He talked privately to her and Pip before calling an emergency committee meeting. Rebecca denied provocation, of course, though the fact that she was in bed with self-diagnosed 'flu at the time of the assault gives pause for thought. Both women took an impassioned *save-our-innocent-sisters* line.'

'Hardly typical of the Becky of *Becky Bites.*'

'Hardly. And in retrospect Ambrose agrees. It hadn't escaped the bird-watchers at High Table that she was putting herself about rather freely among her male peers. Anyhow, she and Pip pressed Sir Desmond for a written confession from Siddons. There was to be an addendum promising total and lifelong secrecy. The completed document was to be approved by them and by Rebecca's fiancé before being deposited with Disciplinary Committee records. Siddons was to submit a resignation letter citing unspecified personal reasons and leave within twenty-four hours.'

'Cool crisis management from a couple of undergrads!'

'Pip Mallow may have taken advice. She was active in student politics.'

'The fiancé. Was that Rebecca's first husband – Teddy something?' Their year-long marriage had rated a couple of lines in the broadsheet obits.

'The same. Teddy McFiddick. Economics, Third Class.

171

Inconspicuous to the point of invisibility in his student days, Ambrose says. But the heir to a banking empire. Desirable catch for a material girl.'

And what Becky wanted Becky got, in that respect as in others. 'Didn't Oates suspect a pay-off?'

'No. And he's sure Sir Desmond hadn't a glimmer. Integrity was his middle name. But with hindsight he admits that a bribe would fit the facts. Siddons blew his top when he was hauled before the committee. Denied everything. Claimed Rebecca was the stereotypical woman scorned, that she'd made sexual advances at every supervision session. Next day he changed tack and complied with all her demands.'

'To official relief?'

'No question. Scandals can scare the pants off potential benefactors.'

'Siddons got any theories on the source of the bribe?'

'Only a clue – if his word's to be trusted. He claims the anonymous phone caller who offered the deal and issued pick-up instructions was female. That's the worst bit, Sarah, as far as I'm concerned. Suppose another woman student was involved? Our Senior Common Room chauvinists would go ballistic. Which is one reason why I want an observer whose word will carry weight. Well, Sarah? Siddons has checked in at the Garden House. I promised to ring him. What shall I say?'

'I'd like to talk to him before I commit myself.'

By ten-fifteen that evening I'd talked, listened and reluctantly capitulated.

'Could Rebecca have fronted the deal herself? Maybe she was your mystery caller?'

It was four o'clock the following afternoon. The Mistress had removed herself and her work in progress to a ground floor office and Siddons and I were ensconced in her sunny, lavender-polished study. Knots of early arrivals were assembling in the Great Court below. Baroque organ music spiralled like barley sugar from the open door of the chapel. I longed for the cool, gold-flecked whiteness of its Wren interior. For the lost certainties of my childhood religion.

'Dear Becky? The voice on the phone was nothing like hers – deeper, flutier. But in view of her acting talents, perhaps I shouldn't rule her out.'

Rebecca had growled, whispered and giggled her way through several comedy shows before fronting her own series. Fluted? No, somehow it didn't fit.

'Someone else put up the cash, anyhow. Becky was skint in her undergrad days. Ex-army father, boozy mother. So she couldn't have laid hands on twenty grand without considerable help from her friends.'

One of whom knocked at the study door a few minutes later.

There was something in P R Mallow-Webb, B.Vet.-Sc.(1985), of the soft-centred chocolate her original surname suggested. A mallow fondant trying to pass herself off as a bitter almond.

Honesty shone out of Pip's hazel eyes, as she plumped wide, flower-printed buttocks on a Regency sofa my husband would have done penance for. Her introductory remarks, delivered in flat Lancashire tones, left little doubt about her distaste for Siddons' project. On reading the phrase *by kind permission of the Mistress* in his note, she'd protested to Ellen in person and been urged to give Siddons a hearing. Against her better judgement, she'd agreed. he could have ten minutes of her time – not a second longer.

Inside five, with the aid of an authentic-looking bank statement, he'd persuaded her that he might have been bribed. Her shocked surprise seemed genuine.

'But by whom, Pip?'

Their mutual first-naming startled me to begin with, since Princes' had a reputation for formality in staff-student relations and Siddons must have been pushing forty a decade earlier. But Fellow-Commoners, being low-status and temporary members of the college establishment, might take delight in flouting its stuffier traditions.

Pip fished for a tissue in a vast tapestry shoulderbag. 'Maybe Teddy coughed up? He was awfully upset about Rebecca's reactions, I know. Afraid she might go to pieces if you challenged her.'

'If she were shown up as a liar?'

'No. He didn't suspect her of that. Neither do I. I'll admit that I didn't know Rebecca as well as I thought I did in '85. Don't suppose we'd have got acquainted if our rooms hadn't been on the same stair. She made me laugh. I helped her in practical ways. That was the height of it.'

'She used you, Pip, used us all. She called you one of her little helpers.'

She flushed and bit her lip. 'Maybe so, but she's entitled to the benefit of the doubt over this affair. All the evidence points to you, Matt. I was in Rebecca's room when you arrived. I came back an hour and a half later. If anyone but you or me had visited her that morning, they'd have been seen.'

He shook his head. 'She fixed that. Things have come together in my mind since '85. Ten more minutes?'

Pip hugged a cushion as if for comfort. 'OK. But no name-calling, please. Just stick to the facts.'

According to Siddons, Rebecca had phoned him shortly after ten that May morning, with the news that she was feverish, but desperate not to lose her prearranged supervision session. Would he come over to her room in Second Court, just this once? He'd arrived to find Pip on her hands and knees, having been summoned to search for an elusive overdue library book.

Her presence, Siddons claimed with hindsight, was no accident. Nor was the DO NOT DISTURB notice that hung from the door-handle. After his arrival Rebecca directed Pip's search efforts to a hatbox. Eureka! Her friend left for the library and a tutorial, promising to return at 11.30 with Lucozade and cough sweets.

During the first ten minutes or so of the supervision session a bedmaker had been vacuuming overhead. Rebecca's interest in Dryden's Alexandrine hexameters was clearly minimal, so Siddons found himself delivering a mini-lecture. Then the vacuum cleaner was switched off. The bedmaker's metal-tipped heels tapped down the stone stairs and along the cloisters on her way to the welfare room and coffee.

It was only then that Rebecca invited her supervisor into her bed. When he refused – from no higher motive, he admitted, than fear of discovery – she ordered him out of the room. Excited, angry, humiliated, he took refuge in the ground-floor loo at the foot of the staircase. He was still there three or four minutes later when he heard trainers pounding up the stone staircase. Almost immediately he'd beaten a retreat to his quarters in River Court.

'Satisfied, Pip?'

'No – I don't know. The scenario's possible, I suppose. I'd forgotten about the bedmaker's coffee-break. And Mrs Horniman covered two staircases, so she'd probably have moved next door before Rebecca's second visitor left. If she *had* a second visitor. An ex-boyfriend, you reckon? A susceptible type?'

'Why not? They were two a penny, those wet-eared public school kids.'

'And they couldn't hold their drink or their tongues. No,

Matt, I don't buy it. Rebecca could have found a simpler way of doing you down, if that was all she wanted. And what other motive could she have?'

Ten minutes later, Ted McFiddick supplied an answer. His ex-wife's.

Inconspicuous to the point of invisibility he might have been in his student days. But the ordinary-looking man in the well-cut cinnamon suit brought something into the Mistress' study that afternoon which commanded respect. Genuine, heartfelt grief.

Grief without illusions, it seemed from his low-toned, stumbling monologue. Rebecca had shattered most of them in the early months of their marriage, and completed the process when he'd attempted a post-divorce reconciliation.

'January '87. That's when she told me she'd framed you.'

'She tell you why?'

'To reassure me, she said.' McFiddick flushed. 'I feel such a bloody fool.'

'You're saying you'd been jealous of *me?*'

'Not you... of Princes' men in general. Oh, I knew Rebecca had played the field before we became engaged. She was open about it... put it down to her army childhood, her mother's lifestyle. Sex had been her substitute for affection before she met me. Now everything would be different.'

'But it wasn't?' Siddons asked almost gently.

'She was... discreet, I suppose. Until Emlyn dropped in.'

'Emlyn who?' Siddons frowned.

'Cadwallader. Never heard of him? Explorer and travel writer nowadays. Hasn't shown up at this do, thank God. Roof climber when at Cambridge. He and Rebecca had something going in their first year. Then they split – so she swore – until Emlyn knocked at her window one night in March '85. Story was, he'd been tackling a new route around

176

Second Court solo and twisted his ankle. Could he spend the rest of the night on her carpet? She said yes if he kept quiet about it. But good old Emlyn boasted at some booze-up that she'd made him more than welcome. Wishful thinking, Rebecca assured me when I challenged her. So why hadn't she told me at the time? What else wasn't she telling me?'

Siddons looked at McFiddick with heightened interest. 'Bit of a fantasist, aren't you – *weren't* you, old chap? Was that Rebecca's diagnosis?'

'She put it rather more crudely after we split.'

'And after the Cadwallader affair she clawed you back by feeding your fantasies. Scripted a damsel-in-distress episode with herself in the leading role. She would fight oh so bravely against yours truly, a monster with age, status and sophistication on his side. Too bad the monster hadn't read her script. But our heroine lost no time in securing a replacement. Who, Teddy?'

'She wouldn't tell me. Out of loyalty, she said, and then laughed. I hated not knowing. I sometimes wonder if she confided in Alice Inglis. A lot of the women seemed to treat her as a Mother Confessor.'

'Not our Becky, surely. Alice was some sort of Holy Joanna, as I recall. That's what they told me at the college jazz club.'

'She's an economist – heads up a left pressure group you daren't mention at my father's dinner table. But she was reading for a postgrad theology diploma here in '85. Earned an extra quid or two from coaching and dressmaking, so I suppose the girl-talk went on during fittings. Alice is here, by the by. Spotted her in the tea queue. She's far and away your best bet.' McFiddick raised doggy eyes to meet Siddons' as if in hopes of a pat.

'Did Rebecca know I'd been bribed to lie?' the other man asked harshly.

'Yes... no. She'd anticipated you'd be bribed or blackmailed, one of the two.'

'And by whom?'

'Someone on the college establishment, a member of the Disciplinary Committee most likely. You were already on their black list, she reckoned, after that interview you gave to *Varsity.*' McFiddick rose abruptly. 'That's all, I'm afraid. Should have contacted you sooner, I know, but I—'

'No need for apologies. I wasn't in shape for this in '87, Could you stomach a Holy Joanna before dinner, Dr Baxter?' His finger was already sliding down the attendance list.

'If Dr Inglis is free,' I said coldly, sure that Siddons would meet his match in the International Director of Debtwatch, whose tussles with the World Bank I'd admired from afar. And I wasn't disappointed.

Frustration showed in his tense, forward-leaning posture as he asked, 'Teddy McFiddick reckons you may know who tried to make Rebecca. Am I right?'

'Yes. Some days after the event. I was at home the day it happened – a family bereavement.'

'Well – don't I deserve to be told?'

'I'm sorry, but a confidence is a confidence.'

There was nothing of the ascetic in Alice's appearance. Silver combs anchored her coiled black hair, her eye colour was precisely echoed in her violet silk suit. She was, none the less, a woman of principle.

'But she's dead, for Christ's sake—'

My hand reached for a buzzer. 'You're out of order, Mr Siddons. No harassment.'

'I... sorry.'

'That's all right, Matt. Believe me or not as you choose, but I'd no reason until this evening to suspect your resignation had anything to do with poor Rebecca.' Her

178

voice faltered for the first time on the dead woman's name.

'Now you do. Doesn't that make a difference, woman? Doesn't that make any bloody diff—'

'Not interrupting, I hope?' Lady Veronica Coombes rapped the study door and flung it open without waiting for an invitation. 'Apologies, Sarah, Matt. Can't think why you've been dragged into this sad affair, Alice.' The younger woman stood up and they exchanged kisses.

'Don't distress yourself, Ronnie. I was just on my way to Hall. Are you coming?'

'Not just yet, dear.'

'Nice timing, Lady Veronica,' Siddons sneered.

'So necessary in farce,' she snapped with the relish beloved of her *Any Questions* fans. 'Don't suppose you've ever been hooked on amateur drama, either of you? Des and I used to make a big thing of our Christmas pantos at the Lodge. Wonder if Ellen keeps up the tradition?'

Siddons yawned. 'If this is a social call, Lady Veronica—'

'You'd like to take a rain-check. So would Sarah, I'm sure. We've imposed on you dreadfully. No, Matt, I've come with a proposition. From what I've seen of the comings and goings, I'd guess you've ruined several people's weekends already to little purpose.'

'So you'd like me to pack it in? That's rich, all things considered.'

'I'd like you to give me a chance to answer two of the questions you raised with Ellen. The two that matter. A few minutes should suffice – either before or after dinner. The details can be filled in and documented later in London. Interested?'

Siddons caught my eye. 'Now or later, Dr Baxter?'

Hunger gnawed, but Ronnie Coombes was not one to waste words or other people's time. 'Now, please.'

'Good.' As Ronnie took her seat on the sofa and parked

her ancient beadwork bag beside her, my mind flashed back to my last sighting of her in formal dress. She'd been clutching two handbags that December night, her own and Rebecca Voysey's.

Siddons eyed her with barely concealed contempt. 'So you know who bribed me and why, Lady V? Not Sir Desmond, surely?'

'Lord, no. Des would never have condoned such a thing. And as you must have gathered, he accepted Rebecca's version of events.'

'You saw through her?'

'With the benefit of more reliable evidence. Don't suppose Mrs Horniman's name means anything?'

My stomach prompted me to butt in. 'Rebecca's bedmaker. Pip Mallow-Webb mentioned her.'

'Splendid woman. Talked her into signing up for the Open University in '86, but Alzheimer's struck, alas, half-way through her third year. Thoroughly sensible type. Offered a shoulder to cry on if required, never pried or gossiped. The same couldn't be said for our women dons, or the college nurse, so I encouraged Kath Horniman and her colleagues to bring serious concerns to me.'

Siddons snorted. 'Becky must have kept you busy.'

'Not at all. Kath knew that in ordinary circumstances she was well able to look after herself. But she'd complained of flu symptoms on the morning of the alleged assault. So after our coffee break Kath decided to offer her a hot drink. Half-way up the stairs she heard Rebecca moan, then shout, *"Stop, stop."* Then she heard a string of apologies in another voice.'

'Whose?'

'Not yours, certainly, Matt. Beyond that, I've no idea. Kath was in two minds whether to report the episode, but in view of Rebecca's subsequent charade I was damn glad she did. When Des gave me the gist of his meetings with the women and yourself I realised that drastic action was called for and that I must act single-handed. It was relatively easy. Des never inquired deeply into my absences. I'd recently realised an investment, so there was no problem about raising cash. I felt sure you'd prefer cash. Do hope you didn't mind crawling between the tombstones in Little St Mary's.'

'With corruption on every hand? Not at the time, no. But now... I'm no angel, but people like you scare me, Lady Veronica. You were what... sixty years old in '85? Playing kids' games with people's lives and loving every minute.'

'Not fair, Matt. I had to cut off, to treat the whole scam as a game, if I was to go through with it. And I saw no other way.'

'No other way of saving this blessed college's blessed reputation?'

'Its future reputation. Co-education was still a reversible experiment in '85.'

'*My* reputation didn't count, I suppose?'

'On the contrary, Matt. I admired your early work. Hated what I was doing to you. But there was the third party to think of. The most vulnerable.'

'My wet-eared sub? Wonder where Becky dug him up? She'll have told Mother Alice, no doubt.'

'I'm sure Becky didn't confide in Alice.'

'No? Then her victim did? But I can't think that a guy... so it wasn't a guy?' Siddons threw back his head and laughed. 'That's why the system went into red alert as Becky knew it would. She'd seduced some poor misguided Lezzie! Risky, but she thrived on risk. I like the scenario, Lady V. Well worth the trip. Couldn't make a book out of it, though. Nothing worth reading. Never fathomed why women should fancy women.'

181

'Then write about what you know. Why you took the bribe. The deep reasons, not the shallow ones.'

He laughed. 'Maybe, one day. Right now, your life history looks a stronger subject than mine, though. Let me try my hand at a biography?'

'Ask me nicely in London on Monday. Now, will you dine with us in Hall? I'll clear it with Ellen.'

'No, thanks. Room service at the Garden House will suit me better. Never felt I belonged here, never shall. Till Monday, Lady V. Bye, Dr Baxter.'

Ronnie Coombes yawned. 'Not sure if I can face High Table myself after all that. How about you, Sarah? Ellen said there was quiche in the pantry.'

'Much nicer, but can we talk a bit first?' My day's work for Ellen was done. But my conscience wouldn't let me stop there. 'You got in touch with Rebecca again, didn't you?'

Ronnie bit her lip. 'After I took on the Beeb job, yes. Matt Siddons was right – I'd helped to corrupt her by backing up her lie.'

'She'd been damaged long before that.'

'Yes. How badly I hadn't realised till those last few months. If I'd intervened earlier, coaxed her to see a shrink, things might have been different... But she wouldn't have taken my advice, I suppose. It was only in the last few months, when her other friends and lovers had given up on her, that she came to depend on me. She'd ring me up at all hours, asking me round to her flat because she couldn't bear to be alone. But I couldn't help... no one could.' She choked back a sob.

'Talking helps, listening helps.'

'I was never a good listener, Sarah, like you or Alice or Kath. I'm a doer. When Rebecca told me she'd asked Matt Siddons on to her show I had to put a stop to it. It wasn't the scandal I cared most about then. Or Princes'. It was Rebecca.

Siddons would have pulverised her the way she was. And I'd come to love her. I was determined she'd die a success.'

Success, failure. So Ronnie, forward-thinking in so many ways, worshipped the gods of the Past Masters of Princes' on the walls around us.

'I knew what might have to be done and that I was the person to do it.' The old arrogance had returned to her voice. 'But don't worry, Sarah. It didn't come to that. I'd given her until the end of the month. Found her dead on the twenty-seventh.' She choked again.

'*You* found her, Ronnie? Don't remember reading that in the newspaper reports.'

'Never told anyone but you, Sarah. I left her curled up like a half-starved cat for the cleaner to find. Couldn't stomach the thought of the inquest, you see. All that listening.'

An Odd Coincidence

James Pattinson

James Pattinson was born in Norfolk, educated at Thetford Grammar School, and served in the Maritime Royal Artillery in World War Two. His first published novel, *Soldier, Sail North,* came out in 1954 and his ninetieth novel, *The Telephone Murders,* was published in May 1994. His books have been published in the USA and translated into many European languages. Numerous short stories have appeared in magazines and anthologies, and many have been broadcast by the BBC. He also has two three-act plays in print, which have been widely performed in the UK and other countries.

It was in the early nineteen-twenties that I went to live with my Aunt Judith. The Great War, which was supposed to end all wars but in the event did nothing of the sort, had only recently ended, and farm labourers could still be seen wearing remnants of khaki uniform as they went about their daily work in the fields.

I was eight years old at the time, and as I remember it was a hot dry summer in East Anglia, with many of the wells in country districts running dry and cottagers having to walk long distances to fetch pails of water. But Aunt Judith was a townie and had piped water, which was something quite new to me, coming as I did from a small village and being used to a pump over the kitchen sink rather than a tap. She had mains gas too, which gave the house a curious and not altogether pleasant odour; but this was something else one soon got used to.

The reason I went to live with my aunt was that both my parents had been killed in an accident with a horse and trap. The horse had taken a sudden fright and had reared up, overturning the trap and throwing my parents into the path of a yellow omnibus which was approaching in a cloud of chalk dust at a speed of at least thirty miles per hour.

Thus was I made an orphan at an early age by the fortuitous intervention of a vehicle of the United Bus Company going about its lawful business of conveying passengers to the fine old city of Norwich. And it was in Norwich as a consequence of this tragic accident that I was to spend the next few years of my life, entrusted to the care of a maiden aunt who appeared to be the only relation prepared to undertake the responsibility.

At the time when I came under her care Aunt Judith was aged about thirty-five and earned a somewhat meagre living by taking in lodgers, whom she invariably referred to as her 'young gentlemen', for they were all male, though some at least were not particularly young. She had a ramshackle old house in an unfashionable part of the city and employed a succession of small maidservants who all appeared to have damp hands, black stockings, untidy hair and permanent colds in the head.

Aunt Judith was a tall, lean woman with bones protruding here and there like a kind of defence system designed to repulse any attacks on her person. She was not naturally affectionate, and kissed me only on special occasions such as my birthday and Christmas. She had a pervading aroma of starch and peppermint, and there was a small mole on her left cheek.

I must have been about ten when Mr Portman took up residence in the house. He was a plump man with lank black hair, a bulbous nose and watery eyes. I remember the first words he said to me. They were, 'Well, young feller-me-lad, and what have you been doing to make the world go round today?'

I hadn't been doing anything to make the world go round, and I told him so. He gave a wheezy laugh and said, 'Never mind; I expect it'll manage to keep going all the same.'

Most of Aunt Judith's young gentlemen worked in offices or shops, but Mr Portman was an exception. I could never discover exactly what he did for a living, but he used to leave the house with a small suitcase and we had no idea quite when he would be back. Sometimes he was away for days, but just when I had begun to have hopes that he had gone for good he would appear again as jovial as ever, with the suitcase in one hand and his bowler hat perched on his head at a rakish angle.

The reason I hoped he would go away and never return was that, young as I was, I could see that he intended to marry Aunt Judith; and I could think of nothing more undesirable than having him for a step-uncle, or whatever the correct term might have been. Already he had taken to addressing her as Judy, which was a familiarity that no one else had ever had the temerity to venture upon. Then she started calling him Fred, and a week or two later he bought her an engagement ring.

She broke the news to me after the young gentlemen had all gone off to work. 'Mr Portman has done me the honour of asking me to become his wife.'

I couldn't see what honour there was in that, but I had the good sense not to tell Aunt Judith so. All I said was, 'Are they real diamonds in that ring or just bits of glass?'

She looked quite taken aback by the question. 'How can you suggest such a thing? Surely you don't imagine that a man like Mr Portman would stoop to buying imitation jewellery.'

The fact was I could think of nothing more likely, and I was not at all sure that Aunt Judith didn't have a few doubts herself, for I discovered her giving the ring a pretty close examination with a magnifying glass when she thought no one was looking. But it made no difference to the situation.

They were married very quietly at a church nearby. Mr Portman's relations seemed to be as scarce as Aunt Judith's; certainly none turned up for the ceremony. The bride was given away by the oldest young gentleman, while another acted as best man. Afterwards we all went back to the house for ham sandwiches and port wine; and that was that. There was to be no honeymoon. As Aunt Judith said, who was to look after the young gentlemen if she went gallivanting off to London or Brighton? Not to mention the expense.

Mr Portman agreed with her entirely. 'Business first, my dear; that's what I always say. Business before pleasure.'

They had been married some two or three weeks when Mr Portman suggested that he ought to take out an assurance policy on the life of his recently acquired partner in marriage. There were just the three of us in the sitting-room at the time. I was reading *Treasure Island,* Aunt Judith was darning a pair of socks and Mr Portman was smoking his pipe.

'Not that any pecuniary return could possibly compensate me for the loss of your delightful company, my dear. But if it should so happen that you were to be untimely snatched from my loving bosom, which God forbid, a trifle to defray the funeral expenses and so forth might not come amiss. There's the boy to think of, for one thing.'

Aunt Judith considered this proposal a while before giving her verdict on it. Then she said, 'I think it is an excellent idea; but hasn't the possibility occurred to you that you may perhaps be the first to depart for a better world?'

From the way in which Mr Portman went red in the face and sucked hard at his pipe I gathered it had not. In fact he seemed quite stunned by the suggestion, and for the moment was struck completely dumb.

Then my aunt said calmly, 'I think both our lives ought to be insured, yours as well as mine. Don't you think that would be the most equitable arrangement?'

It was obvious that Mr Portman had had nothing of this sort in mind and wasn't much taken with the idea; but it was so reasonable that he could put forward no logical objection. So finally it was agreed that each of them should take out a policy for five thousand pounds on the other's life.

About a month later Mr Portman suggested a trip to Yarmouth.

'It will do you good, my love. A day by the sea. You're looking a bit peaky. A breath of ozone will be just what the doctor ordered.'

Aunt Judith raised objections. 'The young gentlemen, Fred—'

'Never mind them. They can have a cold supper for once. Maria can see to that.' Maria was the current small maidservant. 'No need to be back too late.'

Aunt Judith took a little time to be persuaded, but in the end she gave way. 'It'll be a nice outing for Peter.'

Mr Portman glanced at me with a rather sour expression, and I guessed that he had not been bargaining for a third member of the party. But it was the summer holiday and Aunt Judith insisted that I should go too.

We made the journey by train, and all the way Mr Portman was saying what splendid weather it was and taking as much credit upon himself as if he had ordered it especially for us.

We spent most of the morning on the beach midway between the two piers, sitting on deck chairs as a lot of other people were doing. Mr Portman was wearing a straw hat, a blue serge suit and an open-necked cricket shirt. After he had been sitting in the sun for a couple of hours he looked as though he had been lightly boiled. At half past twelve we went to a restaurant for lunch, and in the afternoon Mr Portman suggested that, as the sea was so calm, we might go for a row.

Aunt Judith asked him whether he could manage a boat, and he laughed and said that in his younger days he had been one of the finest oarsmen in the country.

'Come along. If I had more time I'd row you across to Holland and back.'

The boat he hired was not a very big one, and Aunt Judith and I sat in the stern while Mr Portman took the oars. He was not quite as expert as he would have had us believe, but you could see that this was by no means the first time he had handled a boat. It was not long before we had left even the most powerful swimmers far behind, and though Mr Portman had taken off his jacket and rolled his shirt-sleeves up above the elbow, he was sweating freely and his complexion had darkened quite considerably.

Aunt Judith seemed concerned. 'Don't you think you ought to rest a while? You look terribly hot.'

But Mr Portman ridiculed the idea. 'Just getting into my rhythm. Could go on like this for hours.'

When at last he did stop rowing, the people on the beach were no more than specks in the distance and even the bathing machines looked quite small. There was not a cloud in the sky and the sea was like a sheet of pale blue glass.

Mr Portman shipped the oars and gave a sigh of contentment. 'Delightful. Simply delightful. Far from the madding crowd and all that sort of thing. My love, would you be so kind as to pass me my jacket? I shall smoke a pipe of tobacco and contemplate this pleasant scene.'

Aunt Judith had the jacket on her lap. She held it out to Mr Portman but could not quite reach him. She stood up just as he also got to his feet. The boat heeled over and he gave an urgent warning.

'Careful now! Careful!'

He took a step towards Aunt Judith, stretching out his hand as though to take the jacket. And then it happened.

Now I can't say for certain that he deliberately pushed Aunt Judith; it may have been an accident. I mean to say, he may have stumbled; and in a situation like that the instinctive thing would be to grab the nearest object in order to restore one's balance. And of course the nearest object happened to be my aunt. Unfortunately, her footing was no more stable than Mr Portman's, and when his hand fell on her shoulder she staggered backwards and tumbled overboard.

Mr Portman avoided following her with some apparent difficulty and came to rest on his knees in the bottom of the boat with both hands on the gunwale.

I rather expected him to plunge in to the rescue; it would have been the noble thing to do. But all he did was to start shouting for help at the top of his voice. And this of course was a thoroughly useless procedure, seeing that there was no help available within a distance of at least a mile.

Not that Aunt Judith needed any help; she was a good swimmer, and even hampered as she was by her clothing she was able to get back to the boat quite easily. I have never been sure whether Mr Portman did in fact reach out to pull her in or whether she simply grabbed his arms; but however it was, the next thing that happened was that he was dragged overboard and was in the water too.

I gave Aunt Judith a hand and she was very soon back in the boat, sopping wet but otherwise none the worse for her immersion. Mr Portman, however, was in a bad way. It was easy to see that, though he might have been rather good at rowing, he was no swimmer. He was splashing around in utter panic and screaming again for help, this time on his own account.

Aunt Judith shouted to him to stay calm. 'It's all right, Fred. We'll rescue you. Never fear.'

By now the boat had drifted away from him and he was out of reach, so she picked up one of the oars and held it out to him. The idea was sound enough, but something went sadly wrong. I suppose the oar was a bit too heavy for her to manage, or maybe her aim was at fault. Whatever the reason, the result was that the blade struck Mr Portman on the head with a nasty thudding sound, and since he had already lost his hat there remained nothing to soften the blow except a few damp strands of hair.

I shall never forget the expression on his face; he looked scared and hurt of course; that was only natural in the circumstances; but he also looked puzzled. It was as though he just could not understand how things had gone so terribly wrong for him.

A moment later he had disappeared from sight and I never saw him again.

Everybody was very sympathetic, not only the young gentlemen but even the insurance man. 'It just shows,' he said, 'how wise it is to insure. One never knows what may happen. There are pitfalls all around.'

Aunt Judith agreed. 'Indeed yes. In the midst of life we are in death. And though nothing of a material nature can even begin to compensate for the loss of a dear departed husband, five thousand pounds is some small consolation.'

She gave one or two dry sobs and blew her nose loudly in her handkerchief.

It was in fact to be more than a consolation; it became the foundation of her fortune. She decided to speculate on the stock market and did so with such remarkable shrewdness that before long she was able to say good-bye to the boarding house and the young gentlemen for ever.

She seldom mentioned the fatal accident, but one day as she was showing me her latest piece of jewellery she remarked, 'I do hope poor dear Fred is watching me now. It would give him so much pleasure to see how well I have profited from his foresight in that little matter of life assurance.'

'Yes, Aunt Judith,' I said. 'I am sure it would.'

She was silent for a while; then she said thoughtfully, 'I imagine it was that tragic incident involving his first wife that made him so prudent.'

'What incident?' I asked. It was the first I had heard of a former Mrs Portman.

Aunt Judith turned to me with a perfectly innocent and guileless expression. 'Oh, didn't I ever tell you, dear boy? She and Fred were in a boat on Oulton Broad. She inadvertently fell overboard and was drowned. So sad.'

'Oh,' I said. And then, 'Was her life also insured?'

'Now that you come to mention it, I believe it was.' She gave one of her rare and rather enigmatic smiles. 'Quite an odd coincidence, wouldn't you say?'

'Yes, Aunt Judith,' I said. 'Very odd.'

The Bedell Virgin

Ann Quinton

Ann Quinton lives in a small village near the Suffolk coast and is married with three adult children. She started her writing career by publishing three historical novels (under a pseudonym), then went on to write two romantic suspense thrillers before arriving at the crime genre proper. She has now published five crime novels featuring DI James Roland and Det. Sergeant Patrick Mansfield. She is an accomplished painter and exhibits regularly throughout the Eastern counties. She and her husband have spent the last three years restoring a gypsy wagon in their spare time.

The Bedell Virgin gazed out from her niche in the garden room as she had done for more than a hundred years. But she was older than that; the slab of basalt from which she was carved had been mined over five hundred years earlier in Mexico. The stiff folds of her gown were painted in the Marian colours of blue and white with a sheaf of Madonna lilies down one side. She was not cradling these lilies, neither were her outstretched arms holding the Christ Child. Instead, they were slightly raised in an empty gesture that was faintly threatening. In contrast to the slim, almost emaciated lines of her body her face had a coarse, flattened appearance and her belly was thrust forward in a curve suggesting gestating motherhood.

When Laura Gilmore's husband wanted to annoy her he referred to the statue as Pregnant Meg. The very presence of such an object in an ancestral home was an indication that the occupying family was of staunch Roman Catholic roots and the Pelhams had supported the Pope, openly or in camera according to the proclivities of the reigning monarch, since the first recorded member had come to prominence during the precarious days of the Empress Matilda.

The house had been built on the outskirts of the village of Bedell in deepest Norfolk in the sixteenth century and the Bedell Virgin had shared in the triumphs and misfortunes of the family since those early days. Originally from Andalucia, she had come over with Philip of Spain and joined the household when one of the Spanish ladies-in-waiting appointed to Mary Tudor had married the Pelham heir.

She had not always rested in the house. There had been a period in the seventeenth century when a serving maid had had a vision and a Pelham wife, long past the age of childbearing, had conceived, and she had been placed in a shrine in the local church and a pilgrimage cult centred on barren women had grown up around her.

But the plague had struck. The children had sickened and died and Oliver Cromwell had replaced Charles the First. During the dark days of the Commonwealth she had been spirited away only to reappear mysteriously during the Stuart restoration and now she held sway in the garden room which Charles Gilmore *would* refer to as the conservatory, also to annoy his wife. Conservatories, as Laura never tired of telling him, were those ghastly glass and stained wood excrescences other people – by this she meant not our sort – tacked on their little houses to make them appear larger. The garden room at Pelham Manor had been constructed in Victorian times and was lush with ferns thrusting in great swags from the stonework, with a waterfall tumbling into a dark, shaded pool in one corner.

It was in here that Sir Gerald Pelham had spent his last days. Resplendent in a velvet dressing gown that had clung to his meagre frame, a tapestry rug over his knees, he had insisted that his wheelchair be brought here each day so that he could absorb the warmth and draw strength from the rotting vegetation around him. But now he was dead and his heir was Laura his niece, the only surviving Pelham. Sir Gerald had never married and with the death of her father at an early age Laura had grown up with the knowledge that a small fortune awaited her in the event of her uncle's death. Now that she had inherited she was determined that the Bedell Virgin should be restored to her rightful place – in the local Roman Catholic church.

She often wondered if Charles had married her for her money. He came from an old, monied family himself, but by the last quarter of the twentieth century that wealth was running thin and he was never averse to propping up his life style. But she always chided herself for these thoughts. They had married because they were madly in love; they were still in love, weren't they? And it would probably have been far better for Charles *not* to have been comfortably cushioned from such facts of life as earning his living and taking on a mortgage. He could have been a successful businessman but instead he wasted his talents on amateur inventions and bizarre pieces of research.

Like the one he was involved in now, she thought, snipping the thread of her embroidery wool and searching through her skeins for a different colour. He had this bee in his bonnet about the Bedell Virgin, was researching her history and coming up with some distinctly odd theories about her origins. Uncle Gerald had been dead six months and instead of anticipating the running of the estate, Charles spent hours up in the attics of the manor rummaging through the hoards of old family papers he had discovered.

Laura sighed. She would be glad when all the legal formalities of the inheritance had been dealt with and she could take up her role as Lady of the Manor. As it was, she felt as if she were camping out, and there was still the matter of putting their old, far more modest residence on the market.

She stared out of the window beyond the terrace at the formal lawns stretching down to the shrubbery and out of the corner of her eye noticed the flash of blue moving between the bushes. She tried to stem the twinge of annoyance as their daughter Harriet trudged into view, a sullen, mutinous look on her peaky seven-year-old face as she made her way towards the house.

She couldn't dislike her own daughter, that was a really wicked thought, but all said and done, Harriet was not an attractive child. She had been born after several years of trying unsuccessfully to start a family. Charles had jokingly suggested at one point that Laura pray to the Bedell Virgin and she had done just that, unbeknown to him. They had both been overjoyed when she had finally become pregnant, but Harriet had been a disappointment.

To start with, she was not the son they had desperately wanted; and she was a whining, grizzling child who rarely smiled. Her mother watched her now as she toiled up the steps to the terrace, her hands trailing on the stone balustrade, and wondered, as she often did, who she took after with her lank, dark hair and hooded, secretive eyes. Thank God for Oliver, she thought, and then felt guiltier still.

Oliver had been born four years after Harriet and was all that she was not; a happy, outgoing child, blond with blue eyes like his father, affectionate and winsome. It was hard not to spoil him, to overlook his tantrums and indulge him just to be at the receiving end of his chuckles and cuddles and beaming smile.

The door burst open and Harriet plodded into the room.

'Where's Oliver?' asked her mother sharply. 'You're supposed to be looking after him.'

'He's in the kitchen garden. It's *so* hot in there...'

'Oh Harriet! He'll make himself ill if he eats too many strawberries.'

'You said we could make some ice-cream.'

'Later, perhaps. I must finish this kneeler. What do you think of it?'

'What is it *for?*'

'I told you. It's a kneeler to go on the church floor in front of the Madonna when she's put in the church.'

'Daddy says she's a pagan. What does that mean?'

'It's one of his flights of fancy,' said Laura shortly. 'Don't take any notice of him. Now go and find Oliver before he gets into any mischief.'

Harriet looked rebellious and went in search of her father.

Charles Gilmore was descending the attic stairs when she found him. He was clutching a sheaf of papers, a look of satisfaction on his face. He frowned as Harriet accosted him.

'You said we could go swimming,' she announced.

'Ye-es, some other time. I promised Ollie I'd read to him.'

'You promised me *first,*' she accused.

'We'll try to make it tomorrow, eh?'

'It's not fair! You always put him first and he's just a baby!'

'Now don't be silly, Harriet. Where's your mother?'

'I don't know!' Harriet flounced off in a temper and her father stared after her.

She looked just like her mother when she was peeved, he thought. Laura always made out she was a throw-back but really they were very similar; the same dark hair and expression, which in Laura was self-righteousness and in Harriet sulkiness.

Of course he hadn't realised it was smugness when he had first known Laura. He had thought her shy and innocent and had been both amused and impressed by her religious fervour. He had been brought up in the faith himself but wasn't so much lapsed as indifferent to it. Where he paid it lip-service Laura was fanatical, and in the sexual emancipation of the eighties he had been intrigued by her notions of chastity. The price of Laura's virginity had been marriage, so, after a frustrating courtship on his part, they had wedded, and he supposed it hadn't worked out too badly. After all, she had given him Oliver.

He ran Laura to ground in the library.

'I've got something to show you.'

'What is it?'

'Come and see.' She reluctantly put down her embroidery and stood up as he grabbed her hand and led her into the garden room. He stopped in front of the Bedell Virgin and ran his free hand down the spray of lilies carved down her skirts.

'What have we here?'

'Don't be ridiculous, Charles, they're Madonna lilies. You know they're a symbol of Mary's purity.'

'I don't think so. Just feel them.' He guided her hand down the painted stone. 'What does the raised bit feel like?'

'Well, I suppose it's the stem of the lilies?' She glanced at him, puzzled.

'Wouldn't you say they feel like snakes?'

'*Snakes?*'

'Yes, snakes. You know – long wriggly serpents.'

'Charles, what is this all about? What on earth do snakes have to do with the Madonna?'

'Nothing at all, but they *are* the symbol of Coatlicue.'

'Who?'

'Coatlicue. She was an Aztec goddess.'

'What *are* you on about? She came from Spain. You *know* that. It's one of the family legends that has been handed down since Tudor times.'

'I'm not disputing that, but she goes back far earlier. She started life in Mexico as the corpulent, pot-bellied goddess Coatlicue. She was worshipped by the Aztecs and they used to sacrifice humans to her, particularly babies and first-born sons.'

'What fantasies have you dreamed up now?'

'Not fantasies, facts. Sit down and I'll explain.'

Laura seated herself on the wrought-iron love seat and decided to humour her husband. 'So what are you trying to tell me?'

'When Cortès conquered Mexico she was carried off as one of the trophies, but as a pagan statue couldn't be flaunted back in Spain.' He waved the papers in his grasp. 'You know we've always thought she looks as if she's been reduced in girth at some time? Well, she has. She was whittled away into a facsimile of the Madonna.'

'This is all fascinating but you haven't an atom of proof.'

'Ah, but I have! One of your ancestors recorded it all. One Tobias Pelham, writing in "this year of grace 1620".'

Charles consulted the parchments. 'Seems he was a nosy old bastard.'

'Like you,' murmured his wife, but he ignored her.

'He spoke Spanish as well as Latin and translated the original documents that came over with the statue as part of the dowry of the Spanish lady hitched to Sir Francis Pelham.'

'I don't believe a word of it.'

'Well, look at her. Her face has never belonged – those thick lips and squashed nose. Compare them with this.' He flourished a photo under her gaze.

'Don't tell me Sir Tobias owned the first camera,' she said sarcastically.

'I've been following this up in London. This is a photocopy of a photo of a statue of Coatlicue in a book in the British Library. Can't you see the resemblance?'

'A superficial likeness. Aren't you forgetting that the Virgin Mary manifested herself through this Madonna?'

'Oh, that old story.'

'Are you saying you don't believe in miracles?' Laura's voice was quietly ominous.

'Look, we're not talking Lourdes here. A Pelham lady having a bit of nooky on the side and finding herself pregnant when she had no business to be, taking advantage of the imaginings of an hysterical maid...'

'Don't be so crude!'

'Well, it all adds up, doesn't it, and she didn't last long in clerical surroundings.'

'I think *that* can be laid at the door of Oliver Cromwell!'

'Laura, my sweet, you see before you a reduced version of a pagan goddess. Are you going to tell Father Docherty or am I?'

'Charles, you can't say anything *now*. They've built a shrine for her and I'm embroidering vestments and they've arranged a big ceremony. The *bishop* is coming.' She stared at him, vexed. 'Even if it's true – and I don't see why you should back one meddlesome old Pelham against centuries of belief – well, it all happened a long while ago; she'll be... be...'

'Converted?'

'You know what I mean.'

'Suit yourself, but she's not going to rest easy in a Christian church.'

'I think you're doing all this just to annoy me, aren't you?'

'Now, why should I do that? Try and put the hand-over ceremony on hold and I'll endeavour to check out what I've discovered so far. I've been in touch with someone at the Spanish Embassy and he's going to do some research from the Spanish angle This old girl' – he patted the stone shoulder – 'has witnessed far nastier things than we are ever likely to see.'

Laura gazed at the statue. There *was* something rather creepy about the half smile on the blunt, carved face. She had always thought of it before as an enigmatic simper after the Mona Lisa, but now it looked more sinister... She gave a little shudder.

'What's the matter? You're surely not cold on a day like this?'

'The proverbial goose walking over my grave.'

'Where's Oliver?'

'Harriet left him in the kitchen garden earlier. She was supposed to be looking after him and I sent her back.'

'Well, she was pestering me a short while ago. We'd better go and see if he's okay, though he can't come to much harm in there, can he? There's nothing poisonous growing?'

'He's going to have an upset tummy if he's gorging himself on strawberries.'

The kitchen garden was a sun bowl with the heat beating off the brick walls. It was empty. There was no sign of the children.

'Harriet must have collected him. They're probably playing in the old nursery.'

Charles and Laura Gilmore strolled round the garden hand in hand. The overblown rambler roses dripped petals over the gravel paths, and punch-drunk bees bombed around the cascades of blossom. Beyond the ha-ha the water meadows shimmered in the sun, and a tractor baling hay rumbled in the distance. It was the perfect midsummer day, until a sudden loud crash disturbed the peace of the afternoon and sent a blackbird shrieking across the lawns.

'What was that?' exclaimed Laura. 'It came from the direction of the garden room.'

Charles Gilmore started to run towards the house, and Laura stumbled after him.

Sunlight flooded the garden room and highlighted the empty niche. The statue had toppled from its plinth and split in two. Pinned beneath the shattered rock, half in and half out of the pool, was the body of Oliver Gilmore. He was dead. Coatlicue had claimed her last victim.

As Laura's screams echoed round the room, a little figure slipped secretly out of one of the full-length windows into the garden. Harriet skipped across the terrace. There was a look of intense satisfaction on her face.

A Job for Life

Martin Edwards

Martin Edwards is the author of four detective novels with a legal background featuring Harry Devlin. The first in the series, *All the Lonely People,* was nominated for the John Creasey Memorial Award in 1991, and it has been followed by *Suspicious Minds, I Remember You* and *Yesterday's Papers.* His short stories have appeared in *New Crimes, Northern Blood* and *Ellery Queen's Mystery Magazine.* He has contributed to *100 Great Detectives* and *20th Century Crime & Mystery Writers,* and is currently working on his fifth novel, much encouraged by the recent optioning of the Harry Devlin series for television.

Hard work never killed anyone. I've always been industrious; you could call me a workaholic. I believe that's the vogue word nowadays. But genuinely, I cannot tolerate being unoccupied for more than a minute or two. I have to be doing something. And yet, ridiculous as it seems, I might have avoided all the trouble if I had been lazy or shiftless. For all that, I don't have any regrets.

All I've ever looked for has been the chance to go my own way. Even as a child, growing up in a quiet little Norfolk town far from the bright lights, skylarking about with my classmates never held any appeal for me. I did not crave excitement; I was happy to keep myself to myself. I tried hard at school, though I never shone in anything. To be honest, I used to envy some of the successful boys. Like Tyson, for instance. Dark, weaselly little Tyson, who never appeared to make much effort, but all the same, whenever the results came out, inevitably finished at the top of the form. Small skinny Tyson, with his pale complacent eyes behind round-framed spectacles. How I used to hate him.

I left school at the earliest opportunity. Somehow I'd never quite fitted in and I felt the urge to find myself a place where I could feel at ease. But it was easier said than done. Our town was no hive of industry. Centuries ago, so I'd heard people say, the cloth trade had flourished here, much as it once did at Worstead a few miles to the south. Times change, though – more's the pity – and good jobs had become difficult to find.

Yet I wanted to stay in the place where I had grown up. Even though my parents were getting on in years, I had no longing for adventure, no wish to move farther afield to Cromer say, let alone to somewhere as large and daunting as Norwich. Fortunately, I soon had a marvellous stroke of luck and was offered a position with a firm called Farrand's. They were a small but respectable printers with premises just off the High Street, five minutes' walk from my cottage. Old man Farrand had built the business up and taken his son Archie in. They wanted a young person to help with the books and the general running-around.

It took me some time to adjust to the new routine, of course, but there was plenty to keep me busy and I was determined to repay Mr Farrand's faith in me. I aimed for attention to detail and method in everything. Perhaps I wasn't the quickest worker in the world, but the old man seemed satisfied and, as time went by, I carved myself a niche.

Soon the weeks slipped into months and the months into years. My parents died and so I had the cottage to myself, but other than that life went on much as before. And then, suddenly, the bombshell fell. By that time, I had been at Farrand's for upwards of fifteen years. For all the ups and downs of business life, I was content. I felt I'd contributed in some small measure to the firm's success.

The old man called me into his office. He was looking remarkably fit and cheerful. He invited me to sit down and the cordiality of his tone caused a thought to flash irresistibly through my mind. He's going to ask me to come in with them, I told myself. A junior partnership, that's what it is. A stake of my own.

'I expect,' he said, 'you're wondering why I've asked you in this morning. Of course, you're up to your eyes at the moment and I know how you hate interruptions of any kind.'

I nodded. I couldn't be sure of the right thing to say.

'It's like this,' he said. 'I'm getting on – yes, yes, it's true. None of us lasts forever. And the firm is growing. Between you and me, I've never been confident Archie could cope. Not on his own, he's not the type.'

He paused, but still I kept quiet. I wasn't going to anticipate.

'So I've been trying to hammer out one or two deals in the last few weeks, and at long last it's all finalised. You've been a tower of strength, Philip, and I wanted you to be one of the first to know. We've agreed to merge with Edgar, Carroll and Beynon.'

I suppose I must have gaped at him, for he went on hastily. 'Naturally, I'll be stepping into the background now. But Archie will be on the new Board and I think you'll find the other directors very fair. They're a go-ahead outfit, as you know, and I'm sure that...'

Well, he talked for some time about pulling together and working in harmony, but I didn't really listen. To me the whole idea was anathema. ECB's head office was in Norwich and they already had a branch in the more raffish part of Great Yarmouth. They had a name for aggressive pricing and cutting corners. Not my sort of people at all.

'Just one more thing before you go,' said Mr Farrand with a kindly smile. 'I've explained to ECB what a backbone you've been to us all these years. And I'm delighted to say they've agreed to put you on another five hundred per annum.'

I mumbled my thanks and left. But I was close to tears. The money meant nothing to me, I'm not that type of person. What really mattered was that I would be losing my freedom. I had cherished being able to do my own work in my own way in my own time. And I knew enough about ECB to doubt whether I would be allowed to continue in the same manner with them.

The merger took effect a fortnight later and I arrived at five to eight as usual to find men taking the old signboards down. My new masters were not wasting any time. I went to my small office at the back and made a cup of tea. I'd hardly had a sip before there was a knock at the door and Archie Farrand came in.

'And this is my father's right-hand man,' he said with his familiar half-mocking grin. 'Philip, meet your new boss. ECB's director with responsibility for administration, George Tyson.'

I could hardly believe it. My old adversary from the fourth form was smart and competent-looking these days. Immaculate dark suit, shiny black shoes and a keen hatchet face. Those childish spectacles had evidently been replaced by contact lenses.

'Pleased to meet you,' he said. It was clear he didn't recognise me.

'You'll be reporting to George from now on,' said Archie.

We exchanged a few meaningless words and Tyson tossed me a remark about keeping up the good work. The only thing I guessed was that, to me, my new boss would be 'Mr Tyson' rather than 'George'. After they had gone, I buried myself in paperwork. Just attempting to occupy my mind with something other than the prospect of spending the rest of my days working under the odious Tyson.

Soon I discovered that our ideas were at opposite ends of the spectrum. Tyson was a businessman first and last, ruled by flow charts, work planners and productivity statistics. Once or twice he actually had the nerve to complain about the way I tackled things. 'Time is money,' he said. 'You can't do a Rolls-Royce job on a second-hand car.'

I tried to explain that old Mr Farrand had never found anything to criticise, but he waved away my protestations. 'Cost efficiency,' he said, 'that's the name of the game.'

It was hardly satisfactory, but I stuck at it. Hoping for a miracle, I suppose. Things did become more difficult as a wave of depression swept over the industry. People began to seem less prosperous than before. One or two of our competitors went out of business and even ECB closed their Great Yarmouth branch – no great loss, in my opinion. But the job still kept me as fully stretched as ever.

So it went on until one April morning. Tyson rang through and asked me to see him in Archie's old office. Archie himself could usually be found on the golf courses of North Norfolk these days. I went straight up and entered in response to Tyson's lordly call of 'Come'.

He was sitting behind the oak desk, surrounded by all the artefacts of the successful executive. The family photographs, the modular pen-stand, exquisite paper knife and insurance company calendar. He nodded me into a modern tubular chair I had always found peculiarly uncomfortable.

'You may have guessed why I called you in,' he said. 'You've probably heard the rumours.'

I shook my head. 'I don't bother with tittle-tattle.'

'Of course, you are aware that the trade is going through a rough patch at present. Orders have been dropping off and I can tell you we've had to take a long hard look at our operation over a period of time.'

I thought I saw a chink of light. 'You're asking for my suggestions? Well...'

He winced, unable as always to conceal his impatience. 'No, no. Closing Great Yarmouth wasn't enough. We need to slim down even further. And that means cutting the workforce. I'm sorry, Philip. I'm afraid we will have to let you go.'

I stared at him as he talked. I can't remember exactly what he said. Something about how it might prove a blessing in disguise. A chance to make a fresh start. The redundancy package would be generous, he said, reinforcing the point with a lordly sweep of his hand.

But I could scarcely take it in. All I knew was that I was losing my job. The last seventeen years did not count for anything, they were like dust running through George Tyson's fingers. I would be faced with what I feared most – living in a vacuum. Rootless. Unemployed.

It is not easy for me to describe what happened next. I saw his smug expression and in an instant my old childhood jealousy flared again. Then the sunlight from the window glinted on that ornate paper knife, a present from Marrakesh, and I picked it up without even realising...

I can still recall the shock on his face as I struck the first blow. He never believed I could do anything at speed. Again and again I drove the knife into him until at last, exhausted, I slumped back in my chair, staring blindly into space. After a short while Tyson's secretary came into the room to ask for something, but she froze when she caught sight of the ruined body of her boss and the mess the blood had made everywhere and then she started to scream.

After that, everything was confused. Even now, it's just a jumble in my memory. The police and their questions, the prison warders and their wary eyes. The doctors and their patient, gentle voices.

There was so much fuss and trouble and I kept saying that all I ever wanted was to do my job, but no one took any notice. And it slowly dawned on me that I had made a terrible mistake and what I had done would make it harder than ever for me to find a decent day's work.

Eventually they decided I was unfit to plead and sent me out to a place in a lovely village on the outskirts of Sheringham. It's an old converted mansion standing in its own grounds and it boasts several acres of pleasant lawns and trees.

And contrary to all my expectations, I've begun to enjoy myself here. There's a library, you see, and I have been put in charge. It keeps me on my toes, I can promise you. Indexing and sorting, arranging and filing. There's always something to be done – and that's the way I like it. So everything turned out for the best in the end. From time to time, I get a little nervous and ask my employers for reassurance. But they are very kind. They say that if I carry on just as I am – and I can assure you I am determined that I will – there's no question of my leaving.

In fact, between you and me – I reckon I've got a job for life.

Why they Didn't Hang Pitcher (1951)

Alan Hunter

Alan Hunter was born in 1922 in Hoveton St John on the River Bure near Norwich, where he also grew up. He worked on his father's poultry farm, volunteered for the RAF, and in 1944 published *The Norwich Poems,* which he designed and marketed himself. He owned a small second-hand bookshop in Norwich, then in 1955 published *Gently Does It,* the first of forty-two novels featuring Chief Superintendent George Gently. (It is reissued in 1995.) Many of his novels have been published in the USA and in translation in Europe. He now lives in the Broads riverside village of Brundall.

I am not at all sure that I ought to put this story on paper. English law is not one of my strong points, but I believe that a certain tort or umbrage attaches to a course of action which I felt obliged to take on a certain occasion, and which may yet be visited on my guilty head. I don't know, and I hope not. As far as this story goes, I propose to lay my misdemeanour at the door of Christmas Spirit; and I fervently suggest that the authorities do the same.

The certain occasion was due to what might be called 'The *Pocahontas'* Last Trip'. The *Pocahontas* was a long, lean, crazy, mahogany launch which the local Catchment Board gave me one December, some years ago. You may remember that year. The rains of November had been particularly heavy, and they continued through the fore part of December. A week before Christmas it turned cold and the rain became snow, and everybody predicted a White Christmas; but directly afterwards the rain returned, so we were defrauded even of that pleasure.

As a result of all this surplus moisture a critical time was experienced with one of the Broadland rivers on which I operate. The river is always several feet above the low-lying marshes, and at the time of which I write it was fretting at the brim of its dyke-banks. An usually high tide would have flooded some hundred square miles.

Each day, then, pursuing my duties as engineer to the Catchment Board, I chugged wetly and miserably down to Yarmouth and back in the *Pocahontas,* surveying what was visible of the banks with a jaundiced eye. I had on call a floating pile-driver, a dredger, half a dozen lighters and a team of fifteen men. The day after the snow this spearhead was called into action. I found a dangerous-looking breach developing in the south bank, about five miles down, and it became necessary to drive piles for a stretch of nearly two hundred yards.

How those poor devils slaved at the piles! But their motives were not entirely unmixed. They had only six clear pile-driving days to Christmas, and they intended to get the job finished by then if it meant working all night. My Gaffer was a fine old fellow called Jimma. He did everything but crack a whip over them.

On Christmas Eve they still had a goodish stretch of sopping mud to shore up. As I chugged downstream on my outward trip I left them a bottle of something with which to splice the mainbrace, and old Jimma requested me with a twinkling eye 'to be sure to look in as I was a-comin' back.' As I never failed to do this in any case, I took the superfluous hint to have a hidden meaning, and I was right. Old Jimma had got me a superb 'turka', in addition to which there was a little hamper containing 'a few things my missus put up'. Jimma's missus being celebrated for her cooking, I stowed away the hamper in high glee; and then went to see my wet and frozen devils drive their last half-dozen piles.

When the job was done it was practically dark. There was no moon and no stars. I lit the pair of hurricanes which served the *Pocahontas* for navigation lights, and pointed her razor-like bows up the faint glimmer which was my pathway home.

Her ancient two-stroke chugged and spluttered encouragingly. There was ice in a thin layer along her counter, and her floorboards washed with water unless I sat in the very centre of balance; I shrank down into my great-coat and dreamed of firesides and steaming brandy.

By the time I had accomplished half the journey the night was set in as black as pitch. At this point the banks were crowded with alder carrs, and in order to keep the *Pocahontas* on some sort of course I had to keep close in, where the dim light of a hurricane gave glimpses of the silent, frosted trees. In a little while I came to the first summer bungalow on the left bank; and it was here that the little two-stroke gave a snarl, and expired.

With lively language I seized on the starting handle. There appeared to be an obstruction, for it was like pulling at a ton weight. Then it gave, so suddenly that I rolled over in the bilge-water, while the two-stroke made a violent coughing and rending sound, followed by an unpleasant gush of water.

I couldn't guess what had happened, and it was no time for a post-mortem. The *Pocahontas* had elected to commit suicide, poor little swine, and my place was on the bank. So I wrenched off a floorboard and paddled like mad.

When we arrived, I just had time to collar my 'turka' and hamper. The next moment she rolled over and sank, and a defiant hiss of hurricane lamps was the last I heard from the *Pocahontas*.

It was all so extremely sudden that for some minutes I simply stood ankle-deep in slush and swore. I was amazed, and indignant. It was unthinkable that the *Pocahontas,* which had borne me safely up and down the river for three weeks, should play a scurvy trick like that, on such a night, in such a place. With the hamper and the 'turka' still clutched firmly, I swore to all the gods that there was no justice under heaven.

When I had finished swearing a voice said, right at my elbow, 'Jesus Christ, that's the best line I've heard shot since Tobruk,' and I guarantee I jumped a yard.

'Who the devil are you?' I exclaimed, squelching to higher ground. I couldn't see a thing.

'Never mind that, sonny,' said the voice. 'What I want to know is, who are you? And what's more, where's that boat I heard coming up the river a minute or two ago?'

I told him what he wanted to know, and was rewarded with an ironic laugh.

'It's not so funny where I'm standing,' said I, peevishly.

He laughed again. 'Blast your luck,' he said, 'you've

picked about as fine a spot to be shipwrecked as any there is going, and that for two reasons. Do you know where you are?'

I knew exactly where I was. I was in the grounds of the bungalow first on the left bank, a sufficiently isolated situation, certainly, with the river on one side, the broad on the other, and nothing but a cinder-path laid over faggots to connect one with civilisation. I also knew who owned the bungalow, and that the disembodied voice was not he. I said so.

'Never mind,' said the voice sharply. 'Now I'll tell you something you don't know. This afternoon the river broke through into the broad a little higher up, see? There's a gap up there wider than the river. Work that one out, sonny.'

I worked it out, with lightning rapidity. 'You mean we're cut off?' I said.

'You're quite a quiz kid,' said the voice. 'I mean exactly that. Not that you can't swim for it, if you've a mind to, but I've been in that water once just lately, and I can tell you it's perishing cold.'

He spoke with conviction, and I shivered. 'Let's get up to the bungalow,' I said. 'At least there's a roof there.'

'Wait,' said he. 'I suppose they won't be out looking for you, will they?'

'Looking for me? No, I don't think they will.'

'You're sure of that?'

'Unfortunately, yes. I'm a bachelor, and my charlady won't be in tomorrow. Nobody will give me a thought until I fail to turn up at Yarmouth tomorrow.'

'When's that?'

'Oh, about one o'clock. But they won't take it up till the evening, when they'll ring me up. It may be a couple of days before they do anything about it.' And I swore at such a poor outlook.

'Hmm,' said the voice. 'Well, it might be worse. It's a bloody shame about the boat. Come on – it looks as though you and me will have to be bed-fellows.'

I followed him as well as I could out of the alder carr, over the lawn and up to the bungalow, in a window of which I was glad to see a lamp burning. It was the usual Broads bungalow, built on piles, thatched, with a wet boathouse under it. We climbed the steps to the verandah and entered by a pair of french windows, the catch of which had been forced. When my companion saw what I was carrying he gave an oath.

'Blast! You've got some scoff! We shall be all right now for a bit, eh sonny?'

I suffered him to explore the hamper while I took a good look at him. He was a huge strapping fellow, with massive limbs and enormous hands. His hair was badly cut, and cut short. His face was big and pitted, with a flat nose and small eyes. He was wearing an incongruous mixture of plus-fours with a navy blazer, both items too small, and on his feet heavy nailed boots. He caught my eye as I examined him.

'Woss the matter, sonny?' he demanded. 'Don't you like the look of me?' And his two small eyes darted out unpleasantly.

'I've seen worse,' said I, refusing to be intimidated.

His eyes searched me, threateningly. Then he burst into raucous laughter.

'Well, don't reckon I ever set up for a beauty!' he exclaimed, 'nor I aren't dressed to kill, just at the moment. Never mind, never mind.' And he took a monstrous bite out of one of Mrs Jimma's sausage rolls.

I said, 'You found those clothes in the bungalow. You broke in.'

He paused in his chawing and threw me a black look. 'Suppose I did, hey?'

I shrugged my shoulders. 'There's nothing I can do about it.'

'No,' he said, throwing in the remains of the sausage-roll. 'There isn't, is there?'

'Furthermore,' said I, 'I've seen boots like those before,' and I looked at them pointedly.

He sprang up, swearing horribly. 'What d'you mean by that, hey – what d'you mean by it?' he shouted. 'What's it got to do with you, anyway? Don't you forget where you are, sonny, don't forget it, that's what I say!'

'You're a convict,' I said.

For a moment he lifted his huge hand, his pitted face working strangely, and I had visions of being crushed to pulp in a sudden Herculean outburst. Then he smashed it down, not on me but on the table. It was as though something suddenly shrank inside him. He fell rather than sat down on a wicker settle, his hands working, the knuckles standing out like knobs of ivory. His face seemed yellow. His eyes were staring. Neither of us spoke for quite a minute.

'You're one of them,' he said at last, in a low voice. 'I can feel it. You're like all the rest. You're agin me. I can see it i'n't no use. It'll have to come.'

'What were you in for?' I asked.

'In for? Me?' He took hold of the arm of the settle, and shook at it with such violence that I thought it must break. 'I'm Pitcher,' he said.

'Well, what did you do?'

'Do? Do? You ask me what I did? Don't you never read the papers, sonny? I'm Pitcher, the bloke what's to swing for knocking off the jeweller. Pitcher, Pitcher!'

He reiterated the name as though it were an imprecation, and I instinctively stepped back a pace. He looked at me. His eyes had the half-defiant, half-fearful expression of a cornered animal.

'And did you do it?' I ventured.

'Course I did. I hit him. Had to, or he'd have raised the devil. But Christ, that was clean and accidental, as you might say. I didn't mean to finish the old joker. It's nothing like what they're going to do to me if they get me back.'

I looked in his eye. That feeble catch-phrase about a life for a life came into my mind, but it seemed hollow and meaningless. I did not speak it. Instead I said, 'You had a fair trial.'

'What was the need for a trial, sonny? I pleaded guilty.' He brooded for a moment. 'Don't you see?' he burst out. 'I'm sentenced – I got to be killed – nobody can't do anything. The day before I made my break the joker came in and looked at my neck. As he went out I heard him say to the warder, 'Thass a tough 'un, I'm going to give him ten feet.' Ten feet! Mister, I know about hanging – they aren't going to hang me, they're going to wrench my bleeding head off.'

I felt myself growing sick, and could think of nothing to say. Outside the wind was getting up. I could hear it slopping wavelets on the staithe just below us, a gentle reminder of our retreatless situation. Pitcher moaned to himself and went on talking.

'Once you've got your sentence, it's the end. You ha'n't got no more right in this world. They've got you and they're a-going to kill you, and every living soul in the world is with them. There i'n't a single one you can turn to, not one. They're all in it together, they're agin you. I wish I'd killed that bloody hangman when he came to look at my neck.'

I snapped at him, 'Shut up! It isn't my fault. I didn't make the law, I didn't sentence you.'

'But you'll help them to get me again, if you see the chance. I tell you what, sonny, I ought to do you in. I got a right to. You're my enemy. They're all my enemies now. I ought to kill everybody I can get my hands on, one after the other. It's them or me, and I've only got one life.'

225

'You're free at the moment.'

'And how long is that going to last, hey? I tell you, you don't know how it is. Everyone in the world wants to kill me.'

He picked out another sausage-roll, and champed at it mechanically. The action gave me an idea. I unpacked the rest of the hamper and placed the contents on the table.

'Look,' I said, 'what's done is done, and I can't help it if I would. You say they're bound to get you again – all right. But they won't get you tonight, that's certain, so you might as well make the best of it. This is Christmas Eve, Mr Pitcher. Let's turn to and see if we can make it something like Christmas Eve.'

He stared at me suspiciously. 'How do you mean?' he growled.

'Well, for a start, we've got a turkey. Is there any way of cooking it in this place?'

'There's one of them oil-cookers in the scullery.'

'How are we off for oil?'

'Reckon there's a good bit in the drum.'

I went to work, and he followed me about, watching. I found the cooker and made it go. I put in the turkey. In a little while a scrumptious smell began to percolate through the deserted bungalow. 'Did they leave any tea or coffee about?' I asked him.

'There's a drop of tea in a tin,' he said.

I found it, and made some. There was no milk or sugar, but a dash of whisky from my hip flask made it palatable. Meanwhile Pitcher, finding my proceedings were not inimical, unbent himself sufficiently to fill and light an oil-stove.

At nine o'clock we sat down to a Christmas dinner. It was a little on the plain side, I must admit, without any chestnut stuffing or brandy sauce: but there was plenty of it, and though I say it myself the turkey was done to a turn.

As he crammed and crammed his suspicious maw, Pitcher grew convivial. He told me all about his jail-break. It was not his first break by any means. He had been taken prisoner twice during the war, and both times he had made a break. On the present occasion he had engineered it by a clever pretence of abdominal pains. He was taken to the hospital for X-ray examination, and came to miraculous life while being carried in.

'Where did you go then?' I enquired.

'Oh, I works my way down to Carrow Bridge and got a tow out of town.'

'A tow?'

'That's right, sonny, and perishing cold it was, I'm telling you. There was a couple of rozzers on the bridge, and me squatting in the water underneath. I waits till something comes along with a dinghy behind it, and then slips out and catches hold of the dinghy.'

'But didn't the policemen spot you?'

'Nauw! I wasn't in the dinghy – I was underneath it. They never see anything.'

But the crew of the launch noticed him as he dropped off at Whitlingham, and reported it, as a consequence of which he left the Yare and worked across country to the North River.

'What makes you stick to rivers?' I wanted to know.

'I'n't it obvious, sonny? If I could knock off a boat and some juice I'd be over on the other side before they knew what was happening.'

'You mean you'd go across to France?'

'More like Belgium. But it's all the same.'

He knit his brows, and brooded darkly over a second helping of Mrs Jimma's pudding, and as he went to work on it I couldn't help glancing at his neck, and shuddering. According to the justice of this country, that neck ought to have been torn apart with a piece of hemp, some days previously. In a few more days, perhaps, it would be so torn.

227

Just at the moment it was swallowing Christmas pudding. I picked up my spoon. I tried to take hold of myself; but it was no use.

'Pitcher,' I said, 'what'll you do if you get to France?'

He spit out a seed. 'Shan't stop in France,' he said. 'I'd flog the boat and work through to Italy. I know some of the Eye-ties. I'd be all right there.'

'But what would you do?'

'Me?' He sniffed seriously. 'I can do most things in my line. I dare say the Black Market'll be the lay just now. I worked that in Berlin before I was demobbed.'

'You won't go straight?'

'Naow.'

There was nothing to say to that. He was what he was. But it didn't help me in the decision I saw looming up, dead ahead of me. Because when he spoke of a boat I realised in a flash that I held his life in my hands. I took up my spoon again, and tried to eat a mouthful with enthusiasm. It was no use. I felt as if the stuff would choke me. I got up. I knew. There was only one way.

'You can swim?' I asked him abruptly.

He stared at me stupidly. 'Course I can swim, sonny.'

'Right. Pitcher, I'm going to help you get away. It's against the law, against reason and against my interests, but this is Christmas Eve, and by Christ there should be some mercy in the world. Pitcher, there's another bungalow a quarter of a mile up the bank. Do you know it?'

'What – the low-built affair?'

'That's the one.'

'That i'n't no good, sonny. There's people in it.'

'Not now,' I said. 'They're friends of mine. They've gone to London for Christmas – they went yesterday. Now in the boathouse of that bungalow, Pitcher, there's a forty-foot motor-cruiser, and at the back of the boathouse there's a tank where they keep their petrol...'

228

'Gawd blast!' he exclaimed.

'Now listen. When you've got across there, break into the bungalow, do you hear?'

'But I only want...'

'Do as you're told, man. Break into the bungalow and get yourself some dry clothes – you must have those – and pick up all the food they've left, and any loose money you can find.'

'Blast, he said. 'Blast, I thought you said they were pals of yours!'

'Never mind about that – the insurance will cover it. Get away by midnight and cruise gently down to Yarmouth – you should get there by half past three – you mustn't be earlier. Go through with your nav lights on, of course, but douse them for the last reach and cut your engine.'

'Why should I cut my engine, sonny?'

'Because you won't need it. If you stick to my timetable you'll drift out on the ebb, and it's ten to one that nobody will notice you. If they do, switch on your lights again and cruise out slowly, paying no attention to them. That'll fox them and give you time to get out. Once you're out you can belt the engine as much as you like, and after that, it's up to you.'

Pitcher gazed at me with the wondering look of a small child. 'Thanks,' he said. 'Thanks, sonny. I reckon you're quite a kiddo. I'd like to have you figure out some more jobs for me.' He thought a moment. 'What about Joe Soap?' he asked.

'Don't worry about me. I'll spin them a yarn about a man who cut and ran for it. It'll be so near the truth that they'll never spot the difference.'

Pitcher stood up, and extended his mighty paw. 'I thought they were all agin me,' he said. 'I did straight – all of them. I'll remember you, sonny... I'll remember you.' And he patted my shoulder, as though he wanted to say more.

229

He went. I was rescued. I spun my yarn. In the fullness of time, I heard what happened to Pitcher. He flogged the cruiser to a Dutchman, and made his way to Rome; two years later he was arrested, identified and detained for extradition. But he was shot dead while trying to make a break. He died, at least, with his neck straight.

In at the Deep End

Vivien Armstrong

Vivien Armstrong trained as a journalist but has spent the five years since moving to East Anglia mostly engaged with her husband in taming the garden of their old rectory. When it rains crime takes over, and to date she has published *Sleight of Hand, The Honey Pot* and *Close Call*. The house is sufficiently comfortable to draw frequent visits from her six grown-up children, their various dependants and supporters, but there is a lurking suspicion that the Norfolk Experience – as it is known in the family – is primarily for the shelter and convenience of two cats, a Briard and four hens.

'**You didn't say she was** a nymphet.'

'A nymphet?' Daisy giggled. 'Sally, where on earth do you *find* these words? On lav walls? I *told* you! She's Bill's secretary.'

'Looks about twelve and a half if you ask me.'

Sally had come as moral support on this, the first occasion Bill had claimed his share of Benjy on what he termed 'residential access'. The women stood at the window watching the nine-year-old scramble into his father's new red convertible, wriggling between piles of shopping bags on the back seat, his hair as white blond as Bill's nymphet whose name Daisy struggled to remember. Was it Trixie?... or Tracey? The car roared off and she turned away, determined to be sensible about all this. She remembered it now. It was Tammy. Ugh.

'It was good of you to come, Sal. I never imagined he'd bring *her* with him.'

'Just showing off. Giving his flagging testosterone a boost. When are *you* off then?'

'Almost immediately. Before the silence hits me.' Suddenly she felt light-headed, the looming hurdle of Benjy's departure having evaporated. For a fleeting moment she was almost glad: keeping up a bright mumsy front all these months had been torture.

Marriage had done nothing for Daisy Robertson's ego and Bill's leaving home for an anorexic stick insect had been not only a humiliation but a matter of inexplicable confusion to her. Suddenly, the man needed a playmate with skinny shanks whose conversation crackled with smart shop talk? Wasn't her 'naturalness' the thing he loved about his wife? Her stillness, her soft white thighs and pillowy bosom were, he *said,* his delight. Bill had changed. And, quixotically, she too had changed. Daisy Robertson had emotionally and physically *shrunk,* dwindled, like a Victorian lady gone into a decline.

It was that first glimpse at Christmas of Bill's new 'partner' as he called her that had drawn Daisy to the slimming magazines on the newsagents' rack. Really, she owed this little holiday windfall to Tammy. Not that she would ever confess this even to Sally, who would hoot with derision that the person who never so much as won a raffle prize found herself the awe-struck winner of ten days' holiday at Frith Park. It was the most prestigious health hydro in England, let alone Norfolk: the fat farm of the stars.

Already she suspected the PR people had decided promoting this year's winner would be a waste of time – obviously hadn't the personality to carry it off – and the razzmatazz just never materialised. Daisy Robertson was quietly shelved. It had been a mistake. The editor must have smelled a rat because it wasn't as if she deserved to win. She'd let Sally drag her along to the village hall slimmers' group just 'to get you out of that bloody little semi Bill shoved you into', and had never followed any of their diet sheets, let alone done the exercises. After the first couple of go's she'd quietly stopped attending and Sally didn't pursue it.

Posting off her 'before' and 'after' photos with the competition form had been a sort of defiance, Daisy's first act of rebellion. To prove to these people that their lousy diets *never* worked. Being truly, abjectly miserable was the way to shed the inches. Hardly a marketing gimmick though, was it? Mind you, she never for an instant imagined she would win and when the letter of congratulation came she lost her nerve, her blazing determination to *show* these people drowning in congenital shyness. Her reluctance to 'make a poppy show of yourself' as her mother would have classed it, had cancelled out the public showdown.

Fortunately no one in the little Essex village had found out about Daisy's windfall, and the picture featured in the Easter issue had been far from flattering. She doubted whether even her fellow 'dinner ladies' at the school would connect this 'Daphne Robertson' as the magazine had carelessly misprinted her name, with the self-effacing woman who had just started work in the canteen. It was the only job she felt herself fitted for and it dovetailed nicely with Benjy's school holidays. In fact, since Bill left home, Daisy had found herself down avenues which had never been explored and, to her surprise, working in the school kitchen was rather jolly. Also, it was the first pay packet Daisy had ever earned and, as Sally had so tartly remarked when she was agonising over getting a job, 'Look here, love, let's face it. Being married's only one stop short of the dole queue any day.'

Daisy took a taxi from the station at Norwich for the final stage of her journey to the hydro. She relaxed in this unfamiliar luxury, vaguely taking in the terrain like a woman in a dream, nerveless and exhausted, allowing herself to be carried along. The taxi passed through gates manned by a security guard, the drive, winding through dark woodland, eventually breaking cover to circle an enormous lake fronting the house. The mere trembled in the heat, Frith Park, an ugly red brick structure, crouching at the water's edge like a crab about to scuttle into the shallows.

At three o'clock the scorching midday temperature had barely abated, the air sultry with the stench of water lilies. The shimmering surface of the lake blurred into a haze but the sweat which broke out on her upper lip was nothing to do with the heatwave. Suddenly, this Search for the Ultimate Body Experience as she wryly thought of it, was a truly rotten idea. It crossed her mind that she should at least have learned to swim.

The receptionist was attempting to sort out a noisy party of new arrivals, their demands spiralling with the humidity and a growing awareness of the astronomical cost of losing some avoirdupois. The girl dealt with Daisy's registration without a flicker, making no play of the client's freebie status and repeating what had to be the prescribed mantra of, 'Hello. Welcome. Your room number is so and so and here is your key and your personal itinerary plus a list of all the extra treatment programmes you may choose to book.'

Daisy's suitcase was whisked away by a porter and she hastened to keep up, grasping a gift package left for her at the check-in and a plastic carrier bag filled with paperbacks specially chosen for their cheerful blurbs which made absolutely no reference to abducted children, seductive bimbos or chocolate.

She had been allocated one of the most expensive units, the man explained with an air of surprise, hers being one of several 'cottages' normally reserved for VIPs. This tactless response, presumably fuelled by the tatty state of Daisy's weekend case, galvanised her to overtip spectacularly.

He led the way through the garden, past a frankly curious fellow guest seated outside one of the chalets, a middle-aged woman of massive proportions. The sun beat down on a scarlet parasol shading a second figure a few yards farther on, apparently comatose, spread-eagled on a lounger outside the chalet next to Daisy's allotted playhouse. The three miniature residences snuggled in friendly proximity, fronted by individual patios and set off against a thicket of rhododendrons sloping down to the lake.

Daisy closed her door, taking stock of the surroundings, breathing easily at last. A double bed occupied most of the space opposite a large television set built into a wall of cupboards. Under the window a table and two wicker chairs gave the impression that eating was not, after all, a dirty word. The bathroom was sumptuous and the decoration of the entire unit refreshingly Nordic: all blue and white textiles and polished floorboards dotted with rugs. But the best part was the utter stillness. No sound but the occasional splash and muted laughter of people larking about in a swimming pool somewhere out of sight.

The 'wee giftie' as the magazine editor scrawled in the note attached to the surprise parcel left for her at Reception turned out to be a Frith Park tracksuit, beautifully wrapped and exactly her size. She unpacked her case, hanging the new garments in the closet, averting her eye from the full-length mirror backing the cupboard door.

Daisy was still unfamiliar with her pared-down self and tried to ignore it. Post-marital despair had robbed her of her plump knees and heavy bosom, her breasts now hanging like deflated balloons, withered by melancholy. Losing all that flesh had given her no joy. The stranger staring back at her was merely the sad shadow of someone she once knew, a wraith fading before her eyes, a wrung-out version of the roly-poly girl she used to be. Even Sally had refrained from comment, all too aware of the fragility of Daisy's apparent acceptance of her divorced status. It was only with the 'dinner ladies' Daisy felt at ease. They had never known the *other* Mrs Robertson, and her uncomplaining acceptance of all the worst jobs in the canteen made her a sort of mascot to these loud, outwardly cheerful souls who each had troubles of their own. Daisy's unaccustomed role as a single parent was nothing new to the washers-up at St John's First School. They had all, without exception, been there before.

She sat at the table and examined her Frith Park programme. It appalled her. From eight in the morning to eight at night, each hour was allotted to a punishing schedule. 'Breakfast' – hot water with lemon – would be served in guests' rooms, but thereafter attendance was continuous. Keep Fit, the Massage Centre, the Hair Salon, the Sauna, the Hatha Yoga Studio, Self-Awareness classes, Self-Defence classes, swimming, Slendertone, manicure and, most alarming of all, Group Therapy. She sagged, the basketweave crackling beneath her echoing her stress.

Daisy resolved on flight. First thing in the morning. Quite definitely, Frith Park was not her scene. But first, she determined to locate the refectory where, it was rumoured, tea would be served at four-thirty. She locked her door and crossed the grass.

The inert figure under the parasol had barely moved, its legs splayed, the flat abdomen glistening with sunblock moisturiser. It wore a topless bikini, the small, perfectly formed breasts laid out like little brown teacakes on an all too evident ribcage. A tattooed butterfly perched on the creature's shoulder, as provocative as graffiti. Daisy hoped the fly hovering near the girl's wrist, attracted by mingled body sweat and bottled fragrance, was a fiercely stinging species which left horrid red blotches.

Almost running towards the main building, she was passing the third chalet when the fat lady zoomed out, grabbing her arm. The woman's enormous size was impressive, her cylindrical frame much too powerful to resist. A graduate from the Frith Park judo class perhaps?

'You've just arrived,' she said, her eyes brimming with determined chumminess. 'My name's Muriel du Parc. Won't you join me for a cup of tea?'

Daisy's muttered excuses were ignored and she followed her new neighbour into her cottage and sat at the table by the window, taking in the scene. Basically the set-up was identical to her own: the Big Bed, the Big Television and presumably the Big Bathroom. But Mrs du Parc was obviously a natural nest-builder. The place was stamped all over with the woman's overpowering personality. She had rigged up a utility corner, supplying herself with tea-making apparatus, numerous canisters, stacks of booze and a portable fridge. Clothes overflowed on to the bed and a wet swimsuit hung over the back of one of the basket chairs, dripping on to the floor.

'I've been here for three weeks,' she said. 'I come twice a year and my husband insists I stay until I've lost two stones.'

Daisy gasped. 'You might be here for weeks!' She could have bitten her tongue off. Colour rose, suffusing her cheeks in a flush of embarrassment. The woman was entirely unperturbed.

'Ah, yes. You're probably right.'

'You don't mind?'

'It's a small price. He insists on it, you see. Our special matrimonial clause... So I make myself at home here. The staff are used to my little quirks. I'll probably fly home at the end of August.'

'You live abroad?'

'Guernsey. And you? I can't believe such a pretty young woman's here for her health. What calorie menu are you on?'

'Er, I don't know.' Daisy scrabbled in her bag, producing the information pack. 'It doesn't say.'

'You'll get an appointment with Nursie after tea. Weigh-in. Blood pressure check and so on.'

'Really? Oh dear. I'm beginning to think this is all wrong, Mrs du Parc. I won this holiday in a competition, you see. I shouldn't be here at all. I cheated.' This last admission produced no reaction from her unlikely confidante.

'Call me Moo. Everyone does.'

'I'm Daisy. Daisy Robertson.'

'Daisy and Moo. Sounds like a pair of heifers.' She laughed, her chins wobbling in unison. Moo fussed with the tea, proffering milk, sugar and a box of biscuits. Daisy selected a chocolate wafer.

'Is this allowed?' She giggled. 'It feels like a midnight feast in the dorm. Are the people here very strict about the regime?'

239

'They try to be. Just take no notice. Actually it's not a bad place if you call the tune. And after all, we are the ones paying the piper. They've got used to me now. Just do your own thing. Stay in bed all day with a box of rum truffles and a dirty book if you like. Why not? Half the people here are supposed to be drying out but the number of empty bottles floating in the lake every morning would make a cat laugh.'

Daisy felt better already.

'What do *you* do?' she asked.

'I swim. Just swim. It's the only thing I've ever been good at. I swim in the sea at home but here I make do with the lake.'

'What's wrong with the swimming pool?'

Moo snorted. 'Catch me paddling about in that chlorinated fish bowl! No thank you. There's a lovely little stretch of water at the boathouse end where a stream flows in. Absolutely clear as crystal and once it's dark I can do a couple of miles in the small hours and no one's the wiser.'

'Isn't it out of bounds? I saw notices...' Daisy grappled with the concept of this mass of solid flesh in her bathers, ploughing up and down in the dark water every night.

Moo elaborated. 'You see, I don't sleep well. Usually I watch the late night film and then drift off for a few hours and wake again before it's light. It's the best time to swim – sets one up for the whole day. Are you a Pisces like me?'

'Me? I don't even float! And until a few months ago I was very fat and have always been much too shy to exhibit myself at the public baths.'

'What rubbish! Everyone should be able to swim. I'll teach you. Think of it as a survival course.' She laughed, her big belly shaking under the chintzy frock.

'OK. But not in the swimming pool, I'd feel such an idiot. I'm terrified of water to tell you the truth.'

'We'll work at it in the shallows behind the boathouse

before it's light. You'll pick it up in no time at all, I promise. You *did* bring a swimsuit, I hope.'

The lessons started next morning, just before dawn, and Moo was right, the water at the far end of the lake was deliciously cool, the filtering stream having carved out a pebbly beach for itself before joining the great sheet of water which marked the eastern boundary of the estate. The lake shore was thickly overgrown, a waterside walk having long since disappeared under bracken and bramble. Frith Park was very secure. The combination of the lake and the high wall which almost entirely surrounded the park gave the guests a fortress mentality. Many of the clients were public figures anxious to keep their weight problems to themselves and fraternisation did not flourish. The added bonus of guarded seclusion kept the paparazzi well out of range.

Moo tried to introduce Daisy to the gossip of Frith Park but her incuriosity made her an unresponsive listener. She hardly ever went to the cinema and had got out of the habit of watching television during Bill's reign when the sports channel was an unavoidable option. In fact she preferred a good book, a romance for choice, an historical romance for utter bliss.

Since her encounter with Muriel du Parc the ill-assorted pair had become inseparable. After an initial skirmish with the director regarding her non-adherence to The Schedule, Frith Park had, like the slimming magazine, dropped Daisy Robertson. The swimming lessons went well. In less than a week the doggy paddle smoothly evolved into a recognisable stroke, all this achieved in the half-light of rosy dawn when both staff and guests were still dreaming.

'Who's our other neighbour?' Daisy asked one afternoon when she and Moo were enjoying their tea-break. 'She's always dozing. Never known anyone take her beauty sleep *so* seriously.'

'You don't recognise her? It's Carmel Stone. Until last month she was the weather girl on breakfast TV.'

'Oh?' Daisy took a bite from one of Moo's chocolate éclairs. 'I have to get Benjy off to school. Mornings are always too much of a rush to bother with the news.'

'It's not a news programme! You should watch it. Zany. Totally mad most of the time. The presenter's an old actor called Mitchell O'Hare. He used to be married to my best friend, my bridesmaid in fact. Poor Mary.'

'She died?'

'Drove herself off the road. An accident they called it.' She dabbed her eye. Daisy tried to change the subject, but once having exposed the wound Moo seemed determined to probe it. 'Mitchell dumped Mary three years ago. Fell in love, he said. It was in all the papers. Can't think how you missed it. He left her for Carmel Stone.'

'The woman with sleeping sickness in the next chalet to me?' Daisy whistled, finally impressed by Moo's small-talk.

'That's the baby! Crazy for her, he was. Mary came out to Guernsey to stay with me when the news broke. Like a dope she agreed to a divorce and Carmel staged this spectacular wedding at the Chelsea Register Office. Quite a publicity stunt. Mary killed herself shortly after. Tragic... Nobody really believed it was an accident.'

The story affected Daisy deeply, since she had always been a girl with a marshmallow temperament.

'That's what's so bloody awful about this latest thing of Carmel's,' Moo continued, an edge of malice sharpening the words. 'Having grabbed Mitchell – probably just to boost her rotten little career – Mary's death banged the door shut on them with a clang. They're now *stuck* with each other. How can Carmel ever escape after Mary had paid such a price? Public opinion would never forgive her, especially after that slushy wedding. Their mawkish 'romance' has to be

242

maintained for the sake of the bloody viewers. *He* still loves Carmel, of course. Serves the old lecher right! Flowers are delivered for her here two or three times a week.'

'From her husband?'

'Oh yes. That's why she had to be so careful.'

'She's having an affair with someone *here?*'

'You mean you haven't noticed?' Moo's laughter was metallic with disbelief.

'But there's no one here for her even to talk to. Anyway, she's never awake. She must sleep the clock round.'

'Carmel's on the night shift, ducky. She never sleeps here at *night*. Mitchell phones her here at all hours and *always* before he goes on the air at six every morning. The switchboard girl told me. A sort of wake-up call. Maybe he suspects something. Carmel's a sort of Cinderella – has to be home from the ball before the clock strikes six. If Mitchell made a stink about her private goings-on, their TV ratings would be straight down the pan.'

'But Moo, how do you know all this?'

'I've seen her. Almost every night. I found out by accident and I've been keeping score ever since. She takes the rowing boat across the lake, ties it up on the opposite bank by the willow tree and he waits for her beyond the fence with a car.'

'But you can't get through to the road.'

'I've swum over and had a little recce. The walls only goes part of the way round. The final hundred yards is fenced and there are some loose panels. The undergrowth looks impenetrable but Carmel's bloke has hacked a path.'

'But she's not a prisoner. Why not drive out of here and meet this other man somewhere safe?'

'Out all night? Every night? The security man's no saint. He'd be bound to let it slip eventually. A word to the tabloids would be worth a month's pay to a poor devil like that. The girl's face is known to *millions*, Daisy.'

'Who is the lover?'

'Who knows? No doubt someone half Mitchell's age. Carmel's been down here a lot lately and it's not for a heavy workout. She says it's for 'rest' and I suppose it's the one place Mitchell can keep tabs on her – or so he thinks. The new Romeo is clearly living somewhere close or renting a place. It's a foolproof set-up and I bet once Mitchell's out of the limelight, Carmel will ditch him the same way he ditched poor Mary. Do you want to see how she does it?'

'Watch her row across the lake in the dark, you mean?'

'Sure. Why not?'

Daisy demurred but curiosity won in the end. It would be like watching Bill's nymphet cheating on him. It would be a final fling before she had to go home in the morning.

'Tonight?'

Moo nodded. 'We'll go down to the boathouse about eleven. Put on your bathers. I hate women like that. Takers. Spoilers. Like a kid wanting the latest craze and once she's got it in her sticky little fingers, just throws it away. Actually, I've got a little practical joke in store for Ms Stone.'

'What's that?'

'I'm going to swim over and row the boat back this side. She'll be up the creek without a paddle.'

The body didn't surface for two days and came up gift-wrapped in water lilies, strung about with the tough sinewy stems.

Back at home in Essex, Daisy read about it in the paper. '*TV GIRL DROWNS IN SKINNY DIPPING JAPE.*'

She felt curiously detached, her secret stay at Frith Park seeming unreal, a world apart.

Daisy had checked before she'd gone home that Carmel

244

had not yet returned but her taxi was waiting, the meter ticking away like a time bomb. There was no time to congratulate Moo on the success of her little trick and it was assumed the girl was still trying to talk her way out of it with Mitchell. Carmel's sudden disappearance was initially hushed-up by her husband who had half-expected a double-cross by his nubile partner. He was still debating with the Director of Frith Park when Carmel put in her final dramatic appearance.

No one guessed about the rowing boat, the coroner speculating on the effect of alcohol in the victim's body having contributed to such foolish behaviour. Rumours circulated that the girl had been a secret drinker, no one at the hydro having shared any familiarity with the television personality who had guarded her privacy most assiduously. No man friend came forward to muddy the waters and the Press published column inches of sympathy for poor Mitchell O'Hare, both of whose wives had proved so accident-prone.

Daisy kept up her swimming lessons. A year later she had saved up enough to return to Frith Park for a weekend break. She found Moo in her usual cottage. They greeted each other like sisters, whooping with delight. Early next morning they went down to the boathouse and had a dip in the lake just for old times' sake, afterwards relaxing on the pebbly little beach, watching the sun rise over the treetops.

'I swam back across later. Once all the hoo-hah had died down,' Moo said in a level tone.

Daisy looked startled. 'What for?'

'I had to find her clothes. Carmel must have hidden them before she tried to swim back. She *had* to be back in the chalet before Mitchell phoned at six. Got in a panic, silly girl!'

'If her stuff had been found on the far bank the police

would have followed it up. I suppose the boyfriend had already driven off when she discovered the boat had gone. How did you know where to look?'

'It wasn't difficult. I chose a moonlit night and poked about under the willow tree where she used to tie up. I towed the bundle back and put it in my suitcase.'

'You ever feel guilty, Moo? About the joke we played on her, I mean.'

'No. Of course not. She brought it on herself. Cocksure tarts like Carmel Stone think they're better than people like us at everything. How's your breast stroke coming along by the way?'

Daisy grinned. 'Great! I told my friend Sal I'd been on a survival course and learned to swim. She never knew I'd even been here. I've been a new woman since then. Sally calls it my water cure.'

Two's Company

Sonia Kinahan

Sonia Kinahan began by writing short stories, and articles for *The Sunday Times, Country Living, House and Garden, Practical Gardening* and many other magazines. She is the author of three books on gardening, *The London Encyclopaedia, The Winter Flower Garden* and *Gardening With Trees,* and has done two television programmes on her gardens for BBC2 *Gardeners' World* and Channel 4's *Garden Club.* Recently she has concentrated on crime writing.

No, three times wasn't lucky for Sam.

By the evening, as darkness fell and there was no sign of her, Tony wandered down to the shore, and was met by two grim policemen.

'There's a naked girl lying dead on the beach – we think it may be your friend.'

Tony knew it was Sam before she reached the body. The moon was full and highlighted the sun-bleached hair splayed out over the wet sand. She shivered, touched the cold face and stared at the closed eyes as the two men pulled her away.

No sound, save the slap and suck of the sea.

Tony and Sam shared a flat in Norwich and were both lawyers. They enjoyed shortening their names from Antonia and Samantha. It amused them when it confused people.

They split everything equally, and had willed their possessions to each other, as neither had any living relatives. A marvellous partnership and a terrific friendship. Yet their looks and characters were totally opposite. Sam, tall and slim, with hair like corn stooks and feline grey eyes. Tony, not so tall, had a rounder figure which matched her softer, sweeter nature. Her brown hair hung in a curtain of curls, often hiding the extraordinary green eyes, which, most of the time, flickered with amusement. She was a great joker.

Friends were attracted to their warm personalities and *joie de vivre,* but always took care to ask them to dinners and parties together. Somehow even the names Sam and Tony were inseparable in everyone's mind. And that's the way the girls liked it.

They didn't work in the same firm, but because of this they could anticipate the evenings together with even greater pleasure. They got a *frisson* out of each other's company, enjoying the same books, films, theatres and music.

They were on their regular summer visit to a little village inn they had discovered long ago on the coast south of Yarmouth. This particular summer had been one of blistering heat with days of endless sunshine. Every morning they left the inn for the beach early, before the sun burned up the fresh morning air, and so that they could get a good place before the tourist families descended – they were apt to grab all the best places, and the girls had their favourite spots.

Normally they didn't bother to make friends; they left the other visitors well alone, quite content in each other's company. But Charley was different. He ignored their cool stares, squatted down beside them and insisted on being friendly. After a few days of his determined approaches, Sam gave in and began chatting to him. Tony distrusted his classic Teutonic looks, the intense eyes the colour of aquamarine, and the carefully arranged blond hair.

One day he pointed to a white yacht, barely shifting on the still water. 'That's my boat out there, it's fantastic out at sea. I've sailed her round from Ipswich. Come for a trip?'

Eventually, for the sake of peace, Sam agreed to go out with him the next day. Tony didn't fancy being the one to make it *à trois* and decided to spend her time in the local library and museum. She didn't want to go to the beach alone.

Sam returned the next evening.

'You should have come, Tony. He had champagne, lobster, you name it. Look how brown I've got, and it's fabulous swimming naked!' She lifted her sunburnt shoulders in remembered pleasure.

Tony didn't say much, but thought a lot of things.

Two days later came another invitation. Tony again refused to join her friend. 'I don't trust him, whatever you say. I think you're unwise to get too involved.'

'Well, I'm going anyway. I enjoyed myself so much before.'

Sam was piqued and thought Tony was a little jealous, but wasn't going to pass up the chance of another day's sailing. She was growing rather fond of Charley and his exciting ways. What these were she had decided not to tell Tony; they were a bit alarming even to her.

Tony shrugged. She wasn't going to show her disappointment, and planned to photograph many of the beautiful features of the village. She would spend the day wandering round the streets she knew so well. The warm yellow bricks of the houses gave off a honey-coloured glow in the brilliant light. And their balconies and hanging baskets were a mass of geraniums with the scent of petunias and tobacco – their colours like a kaleidoscope.

Sam returned from a day of more boating and swimming, browner than ever, and by the way she enthused over everything Tony could see she was becoming even more strongly attracted to Charley.

So when a third day was to be broken by another bout of sailing, Tony was really fed up and she began to feel their friendship was in danger.

But three times was unlucky for Sam.

Charley, who had belatedly gone to the police station to report Sam missing, appeared out of the darkness, taking the steps to the beach two at a time.

He looked ghostly in the moonlight and started babbling almost uncomprehendingly to one of the policemen.

'I was down below and there was just the sound of a splash. I took no notice, thinking Sam had thrown some rubbish overboard, as she was cooking a meal. But when I looked for her a little later, she was nowhere to be found!'

He appealed to Tony, looking more distraught. 'I turned the boat round and searched for some time, but found nothing. I keep thinking – if only I'd gone up to see what the splash was, she would have been alive now!'

He was dragged away in a daze from the corpse by the two diligent officers, Tony standing immobile with shock. It was some time before she pulled herself together and walked unsteadily up the steps, leaving the pathologist to carry out the necessary probing of her friend's body.

The eventual verdict, after days of interrogation for both of them, was accidental death. Without witnesses, what other conclusion could be arrived at?

Tony, at first, was dismayed by the result, but Charley had produced irrefutable references from the pharmaceutical firm in Ipswich where he'd worked for seven years. So she realised she must give him the benefit of the doubts she had voiced to the interrogating officer.

Tony arranged for Sam's funeral to take place locally, as she had loved this coast and it would be nice to think of her lying near the sea she had loved so much, in a place where they'd had so many happy times together. She had discovered a peaceful churchyard surrounded by evergreen oak trees in a cool circle of dark green.

After the burial, as she was walking to the car, Charley came up and extended his hand.

'I hope you'll let bygones be bygones, as the saying goes, Tony. I was fond of your friend, as I know you were. Will you come out with me tomorrow before you return to Norwich? We could spend the day visiting some of the places farther south. We'll park your car and walk some way along the coast and there's a village with a castle built by Henry the Second. You get a fantastic view from the keep at the top across the marshland to the sea.'

Tony was slightly puzzled and disconcerted by his cool presumption, but nevertheless agreed rather reluctantly. She was intrigued as to why he wanted to see her after all that had happened.

The day was again unusually hot. Tony got up early and put on tougher shoes than her habitual beach sandals.

Charley was waiting outside, leaning on the wall of the inn when she finally appeared. His brief white shorts and sleeveless T-shirt set off his muscular legs and arms, tanned to a deep mahogany. Everyone looked at him admiringly as they passed. His hair was now bleached like an albino. Tony felt wan and diminished in his company.

After about half an hour's drive past reed beds, they parked the car and walked near the sea across heathland. The sun beat down fiercely. They were both glad to get back in the car – opening the windows to let out the scorching air – and ventured a little farther south to a village on a river. They drove down to the quay and sat watching the boats and the numerous birds. He told her that avocets nested nearby.

In the market place they decided on a restaurant Charley knew of. Tony was glad to sit down in the cool interior.

'We'll have oysters, crab salad and a nice Chablis to wash it down.'

Tony was too hot to argue. She saw how persuasive he was. She didn't feel at ease with Charley at all, she wished she hadn't agreed to this outing, and would be glad when the day was over. It was insufferably hot and she felt tired and sticky.

She thought with mounting fatigue of the castle which stood some way down the village and the steep path he'd said led up to the entrance. Fortunately, Charley was in no hurry to start, but left her while he went to watch the locals playing cricket. But finally Tony got anxious, for it would be quite a long climb up to the keep and they had to get down again, walk to where they'd parked the car and drive back.

Even by the time they set off, walking single file, the heat from the dusty path and – to her surprise – the scent of jasmine and fig trees from a garden as they passed along a high brick wall were still pervading the lifeless air.

Charley led her scrambling round the castle till they came to the entrance and began to climb the series of stairs to the keep. When finally they reached the top she looked over a wall between the turrets to the ground far below. In front of them stretched an astonishing panorama to the sea. Tony moved back. Rather a terrifying place to be with someone she was not sure of. As it was late they had not met a soul since leaving the market place.

'Are you afraid of heights? Look, it's not really so scary. See the river over there and those houses in the distance like dots.'

He had taken her arm and drawn her back to the wall. But she pulled free from him and made for the steps, down to the comparative safety of the ground. After a few moments she could hear the scuff of his shoes as he hurried after her, calling her name and sounding annoyed.

In her anxiety she tripped as she reached the bottom and fell forwards on to the hard stone flagging.

'I know you still think I killed Sam, but I believe someone else was on my boat that day. I remember now I thought I'd heard a noise in the galley earlier, when Sam was on deck sunbathing with me.'

He was helping her up and brushing the dust off her thin dress. She stiffened at the touch of his thick hands on her body. But she looked at him angrily.

'Don't try to make excuses. Sam is dead and I think *you* did it!'

'That's ridiculous, why should I want to do such a thing?' Charley gripped her wrist. He looked furious and yet dumbfounded at the same time.

Tony stood her ground and seemed unafraid of him now. Perhaps she hoped some villagers were within yelling distance.

He insisted on taking her arm and they managed somehow to stumble down the narrow path and then into the village and to where the car was parked. They got back to the inn just as the sun was dipping low and glowing red in the sky. She was relieved to see him clamber out of the car. They parted very coolly.

Nevertheless, next morning Charley called early to say goodbye.

When the time came he didn't shake hands but just stared at her, a thin smile clouding his eyes, their colour fading.

'I've been giving Sam's death a lot of thought, Tony. Tell me – just how and why did you do it?'

Tony turned away, and with the sweet tone he recalled she'd often used to Sam, she looked back and cooed at him.

'You'll never be sure, will you? Did I sneak on board the boat and hide on your last trip with Sam? You don't know, do you? You never saw anyone, and now you'll never know!'

Her laugh chilled him as she picked up her bag and got into the car and slammed the door on him. But he rested his arm on the open window.

'But why? Sam was your best friend!'

Her green eyes flickered hard as jade.

'My best friend and no one else's. I wasn't going to lose her after all these years to another, least of all to a male lover!'

Tony shot off in a squeal of tyres – a satisfied smile on her face. And she watched with pleasure from the wing mirror as Charley's figure grew smaller and fainter in the early light. Then the car reached the main road, turned right for Norwich, and was lost to sight under the wide sky.

Photo Credits

Photo of P D James page 22: Nigel Parry
(by courtesy of Faber & Faber)

Photo of Ann Quinton page 196, by courtesy of the *East Anglian Daily Times*

Photo of Martin Edwards page 208, copyright John Mills Photography Ltd.

Photo of Alan Hunter page 218, by courtesy of the *Eastern Daily Press*

Photo of Vivien Armstrong page 232: Louise Palin